CHEMISTRY 11500

Laboratory Manual

2017-2018

Purdue University
Department of Chemistry

FOUNTAINHEAD
PRESS

Our green initiatives include:

Electronic Products
We deliver products in non-paper form whenever possible. This includes pdf downloadables, flash drives, and CDs.

 Electronic Samples
We use Xample, a new electronic sampling system. Instructor samples are sent via a personalized web page that links to pdf downloads.

 FSC Certified Printers
All of our printers are certified by the Forest Service Council, which promotes environmentally and socially responsible management of the world's forests. This program allows consumer groups, individual consumers, and businesses to work together hand-in-hand to promote responsible use of the world's forests as a renewable and sustainable resource.

 Recycled Paper
Most of our products are printed on a minimum of 30% post-consumer waste recycled paper.

Support of Green Causes
When we do print, we donate a portion of our revenue to green causes. Listed below are a few of the organizations that have received donations from Fountainhead Press. We welcome your feedback and suggestions for contributions, as we are always searching for worthy initiatives.
Rainforest 2 Reef
Environmental Working Group

ACKNOWLEDGMENTS

A document such as this is the result of the diverse efforts of many people over a period of several years. The following groups of people should be acknowledged as fulfilling critical roles in the development of Chemistry 11500 laboratory activities and materials at Purdue University:

- Current and Former Chemistry 11500 Professors
- Prep Lab and General Chemistry Office Staff
- Graduate Instructors
- Students

Questions or comments about the contents of this lab manual can be directed to the Purdue Chemistry Department by contacting the General Chemistry Office, BRWN 1144 using one of the communication methods listed below.

Mailing Address:

> 560 Oval Drive
> Chemistry Department
> Purdue University
> West Lafayette, IN 47907

Office Phone:

> 765-494-5250

CHEMISTRY 11500
TABLE OF CONTENTS

Acknowledgments. iii

Laboratory Projects 1

Safety Policies in Chemistry Labs at Purdue. 5

Cooperative Laboratory Work with a Partner or Group. 11

Chapters

1. The Basics of Excel. 13

2. How Do We Make Accurate and Precise Measurements
   of Physical Properties?. 19

3. How Can We Use a Physical Property to Develop
   a Separation Method?. 33

4. How Can Three Small Molecules Be Used to Synthesize
   a Calcium Channel Blocker?. 43

5. How Can We Use Chemical Interactions to Characterize Compounds?. 57

6. How Can We Produce a Salt from an Element?. 71

7. How Do We Standardize a Solution?. 83

8. How Can Enthalpy Changes for Chemical and Physical
   Processes Be Determined?. 95

9. How Can Absorption of Light Be Used to Determine the
   Concentration of a Compound in Solution?. 107

10. Where's the Iron?. 119

11. How Does Molecular Shape Affect Polarity?. 131

12. Do You See the Light?. 147

13. What is a Polymer?. 157

14. How Can We Isolate Biologically Important Molecules?. 171

Appendices

A. The Analytical Balance. 189

B. Volumetric Measurement Techniques. 191

C. Spectroscopy: An Introduction. 203

D. Filtration 211

E. Bunsen Burner. 215

LABORATORY PROJECTS

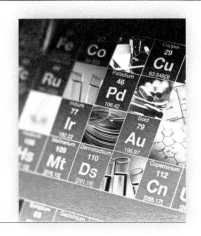

Laboratory projects consist of three components:

- Preparing before lab so that you have an idea about the goals, procedures, and computations in order to carry out the lab work correctly and efficiently.

- Making and keeping organized, legible records of the systematic observations and measurements of the physical and chemical properties of substances using standard laboratory analysis techniques in a safe manner.

- Preparing a report that involves analysis of your observations and measurements and that also reflects an understanding of the procedures, techniques, and chemical systems in relationship to the chemical concepts and principles covered in lecture and the textbook.

LABORATORY WORK RECORDS: THE LAB NOTEBOOK

You will be expected to maintain a complete lab notebook for the laboratory work that you do in CHM 11500. A laboratory notebook is where you keep an official record of everything you do, observe, measure, and etc. while in lab. These records are *notes*, not a full report, although they must be legible and well organized.

Laboratory notes and records are traditionally kept in duplicate and one copy kept in a different place than the original should the original be lost.

Before Lab. Prelab exercises are to be done before going to lab! The purpose of prelab exercises is to help you be prepared and understand the goals of each project before you begin work in the laboratory. Each student is individually responsible for answering the prelab exercises in his/her laboratory notebook and submitting the perforated pages from his/her lab notebook where the answers are written to his/her graduate instructor at the time indicated in the course packet. Late answers to prelab questions will not be accepted.

During Lab. You are to record observations, measurements, calculations, etc., completed during the laboratory period. This must be done in an organized and legible manner. Organize information into tables whenever possible.

At the End of Each Laboratory Period. You are to give your graduate instructor the duplicate copy of all pages from your laboratory notebook on which you recorded observations, measurements, calculations, etc., during that laboratory period along with your report.

Guidelines for the Laboratory Notebook

- The required lab notebook for Chemistry 11500 is the carbonless copy notebook.

- Record the title of the project, the date on which it was done, and the observations and measurements made while doing the experiment in the notebook.

- All entries are to be written in pen.

- All entries in the laboratory notebook must be legible.

- When you make a mistake while entering observations or measurements into the laboratory notebook, cross out the mistake with a single line so that the erroneous entry remains legible.

- Date and sign each page of the laboratory notebook upon completing the work.

LABORATORY WORK REPORTS

Lab reports depend heavily on the information in your lab notes, but additional information from other sources may be necessary to prepare a complete report. In a lab report, you take the notes and organize them into a presentable and readable summary of the work that you completed.

Laboratory reports allow you to illustrate and demonstrate your knowledge of chemistry in a different way than do multiple choice exams or quizzes. Unlike hour exams, however, laboratory reports focus on a specific or narrow topic and you can discuss the topics with others as you prepare the report. In a lab report, you are expected to link ideas, procedures, and analyses to the theory and problem-solving strategies you study in lectures and read in the textbook. It may be necessary to use and apply information from more than one chapter in your textbook to complete a lab project.

▶ **Each team will turn in a single lab report for the team projects (unless otherwise stated). While you are encouraged to discuss concepts with other members of your class, each written report is to be a unique effort by your team. All members of your team share the responsibility for writing lab reports that honestly reflect your work. It is also your responsibility as a team to ensure that everyone whose name is on the report participated in preparing it.**

Grading Criteria for Lab Work Reports

Although the topic for each lab report will be different, the following criteria will be used to evaluate your work in the lab report.

- The report is complete.

- The report is organized correctly.

- The presentation is legible and logical. Headings and subheadings are used to identify or describe the contents of a particular section. Graphs and tables have titles to describe the contents. Sentences are complete.

- The data analysis and calculations have been done with the data your team collected during the lab period.

- The data analysis or calculations, including units of measurement and significant figures, are correct.

- Chemical terms and concepts have been used correctly throughout the report.

- Your conclusions are consistent with your data analysis.

Some Technical Hints for Good Science Reports

- Use descriptive subtitles for sections and subsections. For example, "Titration of HCl with NaOH" is more informative to the reader than "Part 1."

- Organize data and/or computations into tables whenever possible. Include proper column and row headings in tables.

Characteristics of a Good Graph

Title

Put a title on the graph. The title should indicate the variables that are plotted.

Scale and Labels

Indicate the scale on each axis and label each axis with the type of data plotted along it.

Spacing

Choose the scale so that the data in the graph can be interpreted easily. Sometimes it is more efficient to leave the origin off the graph so that the data can be expanded to fill the available space. However, the smallest division on an axis should be no smaller than the smallest division of your measurement.

X and Y Variables

Plot the variable that you control (the independent variable) along the horizontal axis (the x-axis). Plot the variable that you measure (the dependent variable) along the vertical axis (the y-axis).

The Curve

Draw a smooth curve, usually a straight line, through (or close to) as many points as possible. Due to error in the measurements, the line may not pass through all of the points. Do not force the curve to pass through each point.

Sometimes the "curve" is a straight line:

- no dot-to-dot connections
- no wavy lines

SAFETY POLICIES IN CHEMISTRY LABS AT PURDUE

CONCERNS

The safety of everyone in the active learning environment is taken seriously, and your failure to comply with the safety regulations will affect your course grade. Safety policies MUST be followed in the laboratories by everyone in a laboratory. Everyone's safety is a primary concern in laboratory instructional situations and must be taken very seriously by everyone in a lab. We don't establish and enforce rules to harass students, graduate instructors, or staff, but we must comply with OSHA regulations to create a safe working environment for everyone. Ultimately it is everyone's responsibility to watch out for everyone's safety in a laboratory setting. The rules we follow are based on many years of teaching experience in general chemistry labs. If you are dismissed from lab for violation of safety regulations, not wearing safety goggles for the entire time you are in lab, or for not being dressed properly for lab work, you will:

- be dismissed from lab for the day
- get a grade of zero for that lab
- have that lab counted as a missed lab

Complying with the safety regulations is NOT a matter of personal choice!

Complying with safety regulations is simply a minimum requirement for being allowed to work and learn in a chemistry laboratory.

The latest information and policies will be in your course packet should any changes be necessary.

Safety policies are not in place to hassle students. Rather, they are in place to protect everyone from harmful effects of accidents. Accidents are never planned or predictable so approved protection is necessary at all times in a chemistry laboratory.

"At all times" means from the beginning of lab until you leave at the end of lab.

SAFETY AND DRESS REGULATIONS

Chemical Splash Goggles

Each student must own and wear approved chemical splash goggles (not safety glasses) *in the laboratory at all times*, including the day of checkout.

Splash goggles can be purchased at the local bookstores, the chemistry storeroom, or outside of WTHR 200 during the first week of the semester.

Appropriate Clothing

Chemistry department regulations require you to wear clothing that protects your skin and eyes from harm as a result of an accident in the laboratory. Proper clothing for laboratory work protects your skin from neck to your ankles, feet, and toes when you are sitting, standing, or reaching. You are expected to arrive at lab properly dressed for lab work. You will not be given time to go away, change clothes, and return to lab.

Unacceptable clothing for lab work includes, but is not limited to:

- sleeveless or bare midriff tops or low-cut necklines
- clothes that are ripped or have holes in the fabric that expose your skin
- shorts, short skirts
- open-toed and/or open-heeled shoes and sandals (with or without socks)
- ballet-type or house slippers
- flip-flops

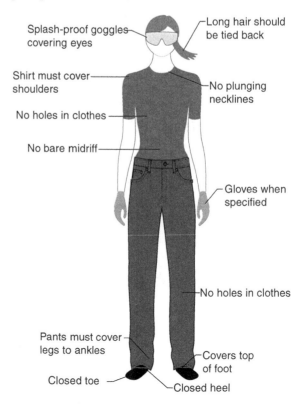

Splash-proof goggles covering eyes

Long hair should be tied back

Shirt must cover shoulders

No plunging necklines

No holes in clothes

No bare midriff

Gloves when specified

No holes in clothes

Pants must cover legs to ankles

Covers top of foot

Closed toe

Closed heel

Gloves

Gloves serve two purposes: not only do they protect your skin from potential hazardous materials, they can prevent transfer of potentially hazardous materials to locations outside the lab. You will be required to wear protective gloves for many lab activities. Do not wear gloves outside of the lab. When you leave lab, take the gloves off and recycle them. Get new gloves when you return to lab.

Contact Lenses

Wearing contact lenses in the laboratory is not a wise idea; you are encouraged to wear glasses instead. If you wear contact lenses in the laboratory, you need to inform your teaching assistant of this at the beginning of the semester.

Hair

If your hair is longer than shoulder length you must tie it behind your head in order to avoid accidental contact with open flames or chemicals that might be on the lab bench. Rubber bands are available in the laboratory.

Food and Beverages (Not Allowed)

You may not eat, drink, or bring food into the laboratory. This includes water bottles. Water faucets are in the halls. If you have a medical condition where you must eat during a lab time you will need to have that documented at the Disability Resource Center in Young Hall and discuss any arrangements to be made with the course coordinator in BRWN 1144.

Electronics

The only electronic equipment allowed in the lab will be calculators and any equipment being used for instruction and learning. Cell phones, iPods, etc., are distractions for everyone and are simply inappropriate for group learning situations.

HANDLING OF HAZARDOUS MATERIALS

You will be required to follow the instructions printed in your lab manual or given to you by your teaching assistant and other staff members for appropriate handling of any hazardous materials.

Main fume hoods

The main fume hoods are located along one side of the lab. The fume hood consists of an enclosure and an exhaust fan that helps remove chemical fumes, vapors, gasses, and dust to protect against exposure to hazardous materials.

Some of the reagents used in an experiment may be corrosive, toxic, or have strong odors and will usually be placed in one of the main fume hoods. Transferring these reagents while in a fume hood reduces the risk of exposure to hazardous materials.

- To use the fume hood, raise the door (called a sash) no higher than the height indicated on the yellow tag located to the left of the door.

- Do not lean into the hood with your head inside the fume hood.

- Materials should be at least 6" inside the fume hood.

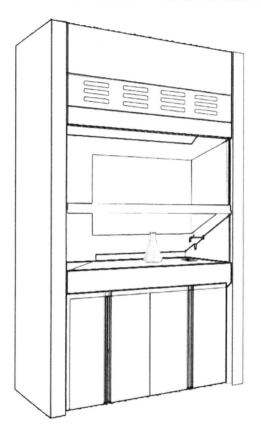

Student bench hoods

- The student bench hood provides some protection against exposure to hazardous vapors while at the student bench.

- Student bench hoods are stored in the cabinets under the main hoods.

- Place the student bench hood against a bench exhaust vent found on the student bench.

- Keep chemicals and apparatus inside the student bench hood.

DISPOSAL OF HAZARDOUS MATERIALS

You will be required to follow the instructions printed in your lab manual or given to you by your teaching assistant and other staff members for appropriate disposal of any hazardous materials.

There are standard waste containers in the lab as well as special ones for waste generated by the specific experiment.

There are waste baskets in the front and rear of the lab for the disposal of items like paper towels. **NO CHEMICALS OR GLASS ARE TO BE PUT IN THESE WASTE BASKETS.**

Broken and waste glassware must be placed into the glass disposal box at the front of the lab.

NO CHEMICALS OR GLOVES ARE TO BE PUT IN GLASS DISPOSAL BOX.

There may be waste containers provided for the collection of materials that cannot be disposed down the sink. These will normally be located in the first main hood. Chemical waste must only be disposed of in the container designated for that waste, since chemical incompatibility can result in explosion and fire. If you are not sure where to dispose of your waste, ask your TA to help you. If a waste container is full, inform your TA so he or she can request another one. Use only a few milliliters to rinse out hazardous waste from glassware into waste containers so as to not substantially increase the volume of chemical waste.

STUDENT NOTES

COOPERATIVE LABORATORY WORK WITH A PARTNER OR GROUP

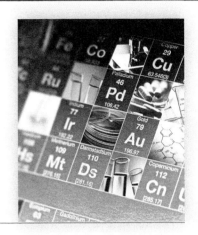

WHY WORK WITH A PARTNER IN A COOPERATIVE ARRANGEMENT?

Throughout the semester most of your lab work will be completed in groups.

Why do we emphasize working with a classmate? The primary reason is that both you and your partner will understand the labs better. Educational research has shown that cooperative group work is an effective means for teaching/ learning science (and almost any other subject) and can help increase the nature of your understanding. When involved in working with others, you are at different times required to teach your partner or peers, which increases your own depth of understanding. And for those times when you find yourself clueless (it happens to all of us from time to time), working with a classmate gives you the opportunity to have someone besides your graduate instructor or professor explain the concept. Sometimes a partner will have an experience that will make a great analogy for you. This means there are benefits for all group members if the group is functioning properly.

BUILDING A WORKING PARTNERSHIP/GROUP

Although most humans are, by nature, social creatures, cooperative group or teamwork is not something that comes without effort. Shared group activities require that a sense of trust be built between members, as well as a feeling of shared responsibility. This means a responsibility to carry your own weight in the partnership/group, as well as a responsibility to your partner. In such a case, no one person gets frustrated and rushes on ahead of the other, and the group NEVER leaves any of its members behind. This may not always be easy. What do you do when you have a partner whom you do not like? Or who does not like you? How do you deal with a partner who refuses to help you when you are confused?

Some words of advice: First, slow down and remember that your partner is probably just as new at this as you are. Learning to be a member of a cooperative partnership, rather than a competitive individual in the learning process, is a new experience for nearly everyone in this class. Secondly, this should be seen as a professional experience, not a time for making social contacts. It does not matter whether or not your partner is the kind of person you would most likely choose to spend a Friday night with, you can still work effectively with your partner. Finally, remember that in a cooperative partnership, both members are expected to take responsibility for keeping their partner up to speed and to take personal responsibility for contributing everything they are capable of contributing. "The whole is equal to the sum of its parts" is especially true when working with a partner or in groups.

MY PARTNER AND I CAN'T GET ALONG

Very rarely do we find a group or partnership that actually cannot work. What we do find are groups with members who are not communicating effectively. If you think you and your partner are having problems, sit down and talk things over with each other. Agree on some basic rules of conduct and responsibility and make a commitment to each other. Then try again. If you find you are still having problems, you may need help from someone with an "outside" perspective. Make an appointment when you and your partner can meet with your graduate instructor or with your professor to talk things over. Don't let problems linger or fester, but do try to work things out between yourselves first. Most of all, relax and enjoy interacting with new people. Think of this as preparation for the "real" world. After graduation you will be required to work closely with people in many different settings, from work to clubs to church. You may not always like all of those people, but you may find that you enjoy interacting with people who are very different from you. Relax, enjoy yourself, and have fun exploring the world around you!

CHAPTER 1

THE BASICS OF EXCEL

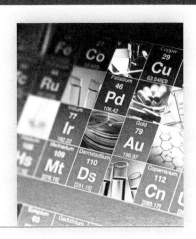

You will be provided with a data set to use for this exercise.

Double-click on the Excel icon on the computer desktop. A grid will appear when the program opens. There will be initial start-up information. Click through the introductory material and choose **Blank workbook**. Rows will be numbered and columns will be labeled with letters. Plan ahead to simplify graphing: enter data to be plotted on the x-axis in a column to the left of the column with data for the y-axis.

PART I. DATA SHEET AND SIMPLE SPREADSHEET

A. Calculations

1. Enter the data set you have been given for this activity: x-variable in column A, y-variable in column B. Use row 1 for column labels.

2. Calculate several functions of the y-variable that you will graph. Program column C to calculate 1/Y for each value of Y in column B.

    a. Place the cursor over cell C2 (column C, row 2) and click.

    b. Type the following exactly as it appears. The equal sign is very important because this is the symbol that tells the spreadsheet that the information that follows is a formula and that it should compute the value for the selected cell. The rectangle above the columns displays the contents of the cell.

        =1/B2

        Press the ENTER key and the answer will appear in cell C2.

Common symbols used for programming the spreadsheet for calculations:

The ^ symbol in a formula means "raised to the power of…"

The * symbol means "multiply by."

The + symbol means "add"; - means "subtract."

13

The "/" symbol means "divide by."

"LOG10" means "take the logarithm, base 10, of…"

"LN" means "take the natural logarithm of…"

"SQRT" is used to calculate a square root.

"B2:B5" represents the range of cells B2 through B5.

c. Next select the cells C2 down to C5 (or the last of your data set). Do this by putting the cursor over C2, hold down the left mouse button and drag the pointer to the last row of your data. When you release the mouse, the cells in column C that you selected should be shaded.

d. On the **HOME** tab, in the **Editing** group, click **FILL** then **DOWN**. The results of the computations in each row will appear. The order in which mathematical operators are executed in Excel is: range (:), before negation on an operand (e.g., 10^-7), before exponentiation (^), before multiplication and division (* and /), before addition and subtraction (+ and –). The best way to avoid errors is to use parentheses to force the various operations to be executed in the order you wish, as is done with an inner set of parentheses. For example, "3+4*5" would give 23 whereas "(3+4)5" would give 35.

3. Before going further, program column D to calculate the natural logarithm of Y, column E to calculate the square root of Y, and column F to calculate Y^2. Check your work by doing the calculations with your calculator.

For natural log and square root calculation, the cell designation must be in parentheses, i.e., = ln(B2).

B. Format and Print the Spreadsheet

1. Change the column width by putting the cursor on the line that separates column A from column B at the top of the column. The shape of the cursor will change. Holding the left mouse button down, drag the cursor left and right to change the column width.

2. Toolbar Functions

a. Select the cells containing numbers where decimal points are to be adjusted. Click the **increase or decrease decimal point** icon (in the **Number** group of the **HOME** tab) until the columns have the appropriate number of significant figures.

b. Select the column headers in row 1 and position them in the center of the column by clicking the center icon (in the Alignment group of the **HOME** tab).

c. Click on the **Page Layout** tab, and then click on the **Print Titles** icon in the **Page Setup** group.

When the **Page Setup** window is displayed, click on the **Header/ Footer** tab.

   i. Click on **Custom Header**. Click in the box labeled **Left section** and type (on two separate lines) your names and your lab section number.

     Click in the box labeled **Middle section** and type Excel Basics.

     Click in the box **Right section** and type in today's date and time.

     Click **OK** in the lower right corner of the Header window.

   ii. While still in Page Setup, click on the **Sheet** tab, then click the box labeled **Gridlines**.

   iii. Click on **Print** and follow the steps to print your document. Retrieve your printout from the printer.

PART II. PLOTTING X–Y DATA, COMPUTING LEAST-SQUARES FITS, AND PLOTTING BEST-FIT LINES

! DOT-TO-DOT DRAWINGS ARE NOT ALLOWED.

A. Plotting an x–y Data Set and a Best-fit Line

1. Plotting the Data Points

a. Select the data to be plotted as follows: Place the cursor over the first data point to be plotted on the x-axis, click and hold the left mouse button, and drag the mouse to the bottom of the column of numbers. The column should be highlighted. Release the mouse button. While pressing the **Control** (CTRL) key, place the cursor over the first data point to be plotted on the y-axis, click, hold, and drag the mouse to select the values in that column to be plotted. Release the **Control** key and the mouse button. Now two columns should be highlighted. Depending on which version of Excel you are using, the order of completing the next steps may vary but essentially you need to do the following as you work through this exercise.

b. Under the **Charts** group in the **Insert** tab, choose the **Scatter** chart type. Choose the icon that shows data points only (no lines).

c. Click on the chart you want to edit. The **Chart Tools** menu will be displayed at the top of the screen. Click on the **Layout** tab. Select **Add Chart Elements** from the **Chart Layouts** group to format the axes, add chart and axis titles, format the legend, rename the chart, etc.

d. To move the chart to a separate sheet, right-click on the chart (but off the graph) and select **Move Chart**, then select **New sheet** or an existing sheet. Click OK.

2. Getting the Best-fit Line and Equation

a. Move the mouse cursor to any data point in the chart and press the left mouse button. All of the data points should now be highlighted. Now, while the mouse cursor is still on any one of the highlighted data points, press and hold the right mouse button, and choose **Add Trendline** from the menu that appears. Click on the box with the type of fit you want (e.g., Linear).

Select **Display Equation** on chart and **Display R-squared value** on chart.

B. Adding a Plot of a Second and a Third Data Set to an Existing Plot

1. Using the procedure outlined below under #3, add the additional plots to the plot of column B vs. column A:

   a. column C vs. column A

   b. column D vs. column A

2. Using the procedure outlined below under #3, add the additional plots to the plot of column B vs. column A:

   a. column E vs. column A

   b. column F vs. column A

3. Go to the sheet containing the original data by clicking the appropriate sheet tab along the bottom of the Excel window.

   a. Select the data to be plotted as follows: Place the cursor over the first data point to be plotted on the *x-axis*, click and hold the left mouse button, and drag the mouse to the bottom of the column. The column should be highlighted. Release the mouse button.

   While pressing the **Control** key, place the cursor over the first data point to be plotted on the *y-axis*, click, hold, and drag the mouse to select the values in that column to be plotted. Release the Control key and the mouse button. Now the two columns should be highlighted.

b. Under the **Home** tab, select **Copy**. Click on the chart where the new data is to be placed.

Under the **Paste** icon in the **Home** tab, select **Paste Special**, then select **New series** and **Categories (X Values) in First Column**. Click OK.

c. Insert a trendline and its equation following the same procedures as described previously.

4. Saving the Data Sheet and Graphs on a Storage Device

Place a USB storage device into the computer.

Click on the **File** tab and then on **Save As**....

Click on the appropriate destination.

Click on the text box by "**File Name**" and type in a suitable file name.

The file name will end with a .xlsx file extension. Save your file.

5. Printing the Graph

Click on the **File tab**. Choose **Print**. Follow steps to print graph.

PART III. TRANSFERRING TABLES AND GRAPHS

A. Transfer and Format the Spreadsheet/Table

1. With the Excel program saved and open, click on the **Microsoft Word** icon to open a new word processing document for your report. Select **Blank document**.

2. Return to the Excel program. Click the **Sheet** tab at the bottom, then select or highlight all the cells that contain information to be copied.

From the **Clipboard** group in the **HOME** tab, click **Copy**.

3. Return to your Microsoft Word file, place the cursor on the page, and from the **Clipboard** group in the **HOME** tab, click **Paste**.

4. Select/highlight all cells in the table. In the **Paragraph** group in the **HOME** tab, select **All Borders** under the border icon.

B. Transfer and Format the Graph/Chart

1. Return to Excel, click **Chart 1**. Click toward the outer edge of the page. A thick border with squared corners and edges should surround

your entire graph, including titles. From the **Clipboard** group in the **HOME** tab, click **Copy**.

2. Return to your Microsoft Word file. Place the cursor below the table you copied and pasted previously. From the **Clipboard** group in the **HOME** tab, click **Paste**.

3. To change the position of the graph/chart on the page, click the **Layout Options** button beside your graph. Choose **With Text Wrapping** icon that shows text above and below image.

   To change the size of the graph/chart on the page, place the cursor over the graph and right-click. Position the cursor over any of the squared edges or corners around the graph, left-click, hold, and drag the mouse until the desired size is obtained.

   Select **Print** from the **File** tab to print your Microsoft Word file.

Lab Report

Your group (of 3 or 4) is to prepare a report in Microsoft Word including:

- Title
- Lab group members' names
- A goal statement
- Procedural reference (title of lab manual and page number(s))
- A data section that includes a formatted data table that has been transferred from the Excel file into Word.
- A data analysis section that includes the imported graph (with five plots) from Excel. Resize the graph so that it takes up about ½ of a sheet of paper.

Your printed report is due at the end of the lab period.

CHAPTER 2

HOW DO WE MAKE ACCURATE AND PRECISE MEASUREMENTS OF PHYSICAL PROPERTIES?[1]

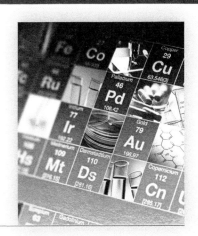

Perform this experiment in groups of 2 (pairs), with each person practicing each of the techniques. Each person must record a complete set of data in her/his lab notebook pages. The laboratory notebook is where you record everything you do, observe and measure while in lab. It is not a full report and does not need to include calculations, results and discussion.

Keep in mind that you will be evaluated on the appropriate use of significant figures and units in your measurements and records.

INTRODUCTION

One of the most common measurements in the chemical laboratory is measuring the volume of a liquid. Solutions are often used and transferred from one container to another. In some cases, it is important to accurately know the amount of liquid transferred. In this and future chemistry labs, you will come into contact with various pieces of laboratory glassware. Each of these has a specific purpose and a distinct level of accuracy and precision associated with it.

Beakers and Erlenmeyer flasks are used for holding solutions, mixing reagents, carrying out chemical reactions, or crudely measuring volumes of liquids. The graduated markings on a beaker or Erlenmeyer flask are only approximate (±5%, ~2 significant figures), so they should not be used for accurate volume measurements.

Graduated cylinders are designed to measure liquid volumes with moderate accuracy (±0.5%, ~3 significant figures). The tall, narrow column makes for a more precise reading of the liquid level. For accurate volume measurement, choose the smallest graduated cylinder that can measure that volume. Increment markings on graduated cylinders vary based on the volume of the cylinder.

The greatest accuracy and precision (±0.05%, ~4 significant figures) is obtained with analytical glassware, such as **volumetric pipets, burets,** and **volumetric flasks**. Volumetric pipets are designed to accurately deliver a fixed volume of solution. Burets are used for the accurate measurement of a variable amount of a solution, primarily in titrations. Volumetric flasks are designed to accurately contain a fixed volume of solution and are generally used for solution preparation so that a solute can be diluted to a known, accurate volume.

When recording measurements in the lab, it is important that you note the uncertainty of the measuring device and record the appropriate number of significant figures. To properly record the uncertainty in a measurement,

---

1 Adapted from "Are You Dense or What?" by Dr. Eric Malina, Department of Chemistry, University of Nebraska-Lincoln.

the value should use all of the known digits *plus* one estimated digit. In the lab, you will make a judgment on the value of the last digit in a measurement. For example, the burets we use in lab are calibrated in divisions of 0.1 mL, so you should estimate the final digit and report the volume to the nearest 0.01 mL. Many glassware manufacturers note the tolerance (uncertainty in the accuracy of a device) on the measuring device itself.

Table 2.1. Uncertainty in laboratory measurements

Measuring Device	Uncertainty
10.00 mL graduated cylinder	±0.01 mL
50.0 mL graduated cylinder	±0.1 mL
10.00 mL volumetric pipet	±0.01 mL
50.00 mL buret	±0.01 mL
analytical balance	±0.001 g or ±0.0001 g

▶ *Refer to Appendix B, Volumetric Measurement Techniques, for additional information.*

Precision for multiple measures (taking the same measurement more than one time) is based on the degree to which the measures are the same. For example, consider two types of bathroom scales. One scale displays the weight digitally to the nearest 0.1 pound. The other scale displays the weight with a simple needle and is read to the nearest 0.1 pound (by estimating how far in between the marks the needle goes). Consider the data in Table 2.2 below.

Table 2.2. Weights measured using 2 different types of scales.

Trial	Digital Scale	"Needle" scale
1	183.3 lbs	184.2 lbs
2	183.5 lbs	182.2 lbs
3	183.2 lbs	187.5 lbs
average	183.3 lbs	184.6 lbs

The absolute deviation ("abs dev") for a measurement is the absolute value of the difference between an individual measurement (x_i) and the average ($\bar{x}$) of all measurements or $|x_i - \bar{x}|$. For example, the absolute deviation for trial 2 above using the digital scale is 0.1 lbs ($|183.2 - 183.3|$).

To measure precision, we can find the **mean absolute deviation (MAD)**. The mean absolute deviation indicates how far each measurement is from the arithmetic mean or average and is found using equation (1) below, where x_i is an individual measurement, $\bar{x}$ is the average of all measurements and $\boldsymbol{n}$ is the number of measurements.

For a data set $(x_1, x_2, \ldots x_n)$

$$\frac{\sum |x_i - \bar{x}|}{n} = \text{mean absolute deviation (MAD)} \qquad (1)$$

Using the example of the two scales, the average weight on the digital scale was 183.3 lbs. The mean absolute deviation (MAD) of measurements of the weight on this scale is calculated below.

$$\frac{|183.3 - 183.3| + |183.5 - 183.3| + |183.2 - 183.3|}{3} = \frac{0 + 0.2 + 0.1}{3} = 0.1$$

The mean absolute deviation (MAD) is 0.1 lb. In other words the digital scale displays the weight as **183.3 ± 0.1 lbs**.

The mean absolute deviation (MAD) of the weight measured using the scale with a needle is calculated below, where the average weight was 184.6 lbs.

$$\frac{|184.2 - 184.6| + |182.2 - 184.6| + |187.5 - 184.6|}{3} = \frac{0.4 + 2.4 + 2.9}{3} = 1.9$$

The mean absolute deviation (MAD) of the weight with the "needle" scale is 1.9 lb. Using this scale, the weight is **184.6 ± 1.9 lbs**. There is more variation in the measurement of weight with this scale.

Therefore, in this example, the digital scale has *more precision* since it was able to produce measurements that are *closer together* than the "needle" scale.

Accuracy

Accuracy is different from precision. **Accuracy** is the degree to which the measure is close to the *actual value*. In the previous example with the scales, the average weight for the digital scale is 183.3 lbs and the scale with the needle is 184.6 lbs. Which of these weights was more accurate?

The accuracy of a measurement can be measured by calculating the percent error. The percent error indicates how far the measurement is from the true or theoretical value. The percent error is calculated using equation (2) below..

$$\text{percent error} = \frac{|\,experimental\ value - theoretical\ value\,|}{theoretical\ value} \times 100 \qquad (2)$$

To find the percent error, we must know the theoretical or "true" value. With the scale example, if the person went to the doctor's office and was weighed on a recently calibrated scale and got a weight of 184.2 lbs, then we could consider this the theoretical or "true" value. The percent error for the digital and needle scales based on all three trials is 0.49% and 0.22% respectively, which leads us to conclude that the needle scale is more accurate than the digital scale.

Just because an instrument is more precise does not necessarily mean it is more accurate.

PROCEDURE

In this exercise, you will practice measuring masses and volumes using various types of glassware and compare the accuracy and precision of the measurements. You will also practice determining the density of a liquid. These exercises are meant to prepare you for future experiments.

Before you begin the experiment, your instructor will discuss and demonstrate use of the following equipment or glassware:

- Analytical balance
- Buret
- Volumetric pipet

You may use either a milligram balance (in the lab, ±0.001 g) or analytical balance (in the balance room, ±0.0001 g) for this experiment. For each task, use the *same* balance for *all* measurements.

You and your partner will need the following glassware and equipment for this exercise:

- Four (4) clean and dry 125-mL Erlenmeyer flasks
- 10.00 mL graduated cylinder
- 50.0 mL graduated cylinder
- 50.00 mL buret
- ring stand and buret clamp
- 10.00 mL pipet and pipet bulb

DATA COLLECTION

To practice using a graduated cylinder, buret and pipet, you will measure the mass of deionized water for exact volumes dispensed with these instruments. The mass of deionized water will determine how accurately and precisely you have measured the volume. Table 2.3 below gives the density of water over a range of temperatures.

Table 2.3. List of Density of Water at Various Temperatures

°C	Density (g/mL)	°C	Density (g/mL)
19	0.998405	25	0.997044
20	0.998203	26	0.996783
21	0.997992	27	0.996512
22	0.997770	28	0.996232
23	0.997538	29	0.995944
24	0.997296	30	0.995646

From the CRC Handbook of Chemistry and Physics, 96th edition 2014

Practice Using Graduated Cylinders

10.00 mL cylinder

Obtain a clean, dry 125-mL Erlenmeyer flask. Weigh the clean, DRY flask and record the mass using the proper number of significant figures.

Obtain a clean **10.00-mL graduated cylinder**.

Obtain about 150 mL of deionized water in a 250-mL beaker.

Measure 10 mL of deionized water in the 10.00-mL graduated cylinder by pouring slightly less than 10 mL into the cylinder and then adding water with a medicine dropper until you have exactly 10.00 mL. If you add too much water, use the dropper to remove the excess water.

Pour the water from the 10.00-mL graduated cylinder into the pre-weighed 125-mL Erlenmeyer flask. Weigh the flask plus 10 mL of deionized water and record the total mass (g).

Using the 10.00-mL graduated cylinder, measure another 10 mL portion of deionized water and add it to the 10 mL of water already in the Erlenmeyer flask. Weigh the flask plus 20 mL (total) of deionized water and record the total mass (g). Repeat this procedure one additional time; i.e. add another 10 mL portion of water and weigh the flask plus 30 mL (total) of deionized water.

Measure and record the temperature of the water in the 125-mL Erlenmeyer flask.

50.0 mL cylinder

Obtain a clean, dry 125-mL Erlenmeyer flask and record its mass.

Repeat the above procedure using a **50.0-mL graduated cylinder** to measure three sequential 10 mL portions of deionized water. Record the mass of the flask plus water after each 10 mL addition.

Measure and record the temperature of the water in the 125-mL Erlenmeyer flask and record.

Practice Using a Buret

Attach a buret clamp to a ring stand.

Holding a 50.00-mL buret over the sink, use a funnel to fill the buret with deionized water until the level of the water is between the 0 and 10 mL marks. Remove any air trapped in the tip of the buret by opening the stopcock completely and closing the stopcock until all the air is pushed out of the tip.

Add more deionized water to the buret until the level is between the 0 and 1 mL marks. Clamp the buret to the ring stand. Record the volume reading to two decimal places. Review Appendix B for information on properly reading a buret.

Find the mass of a clean, dry 125-mL Erlenmeyer flask and record the measurement.

Place the flask under the buret and deliver *about* 10 mL of deionized water into the flask. After closing the stopcock, touch the side of the flask to the tip of the buret in order to remove any water on the tip of the buret. Don't spend time trying to deliver exactly 10.00 mL from the buret, as this is not how a buret a typically used. Rather deliver *about* 10 mL and then use the volume reading on the buret to determine and record the *exact volume* delivered from the buret. Record the volume delivered to the proper number of significant figures (2 decimal places). Find and record the total mass of the flask and water.

Place the flask under the buret again and add an additional portion of *about* 10 mL of deionized water so that total volume in flask is about 20 mL. Remove any water from the tip of the buret, as described above. Use the volume reading on the buret to determine and record the *exact volume* delivered from the buret. Find and record the total mass of the flask plus about 20 mL of water.

Continue this same procedure with one additional portion of *about* 10 mL of deionized water; Use the volume reading on the buret to determine and record the *exact volume* delivered from the buret. Record the mass of the flask after the final addition (i.e. flask plus about 30 mL of water).

Measure and record the temperature of the water in the flask.

Practice Using a Pipet

Obtain a 10.00-mL pipet from your instructor.

Weigh a clean, dry 125-mL Erlenmeyer flask and record the mass.

Pipet 10.00 mL of deionized water into the flask. Find and record the total mass of the flask and water.

Use the pipet to add an additional 10.00 mL of deionized water to the flask. Again weigh and record the total mass of the flask and water (20.00 mL total). Continue this same procedure with one more 10.00 mL sample of water. Find and record the total mass of the flask and 30.00 mL of water.

Measure and record the temperature of the water in the flask.

DATA ANALYSIS

Record the literature value for the density of water at the temperature recorded at the end of practicing with each type of glassware.

For each trial with each piece of glassware (10.00-mL graduated cylinder, 50.0-mL graduated cylinder, 10.00-mL pipet and 50.00-mL buret), calculate:

a. the mass of the deionized water by subtracting the mass of the Erlenmeyer flask (the "tare" mass) from the total mass (flask plus deionized water),

b. the experimental density (g/mL) of deionized water using the mass of the water determined in part (a) and the measured volume,

c. the average experimental density for your three trials with each type of glassware,

d. the mean absolute deviation (MAD) (refer to equation (1)) to estimate the precision of the measurements made with each type of glassware, and

e. the percent error for each piece of glassware (refer to equation (2)) to estimate the accuracy of the measurements made with each graduated cylinder.

Record your results to the proper number of significant figures in the lab report form.

Show your work in a sample calculation as directing on the lab report form.

RESULTS

Summarize your results in Table 8 on the report form.

DISCUSSION

For questions 1 and 2 below, Support your claim using evidence, i.e. experimental data that supports the claim. Cite specific quantitative results. Connect your evidence to your claim using reasoning that explains *why* your evidence supports your claim. Reasoning should be based on a scientific rule, law, principle or definition.

1. Which piece(s) has/have the greater **accuracy**, the 10.00-mL graduated cylinder, 50.0-mL graduated cylinder, 50.00-mL buret, or 10.00-mL pipet? (Refer to the instructions above for answering this question.)

2. Which piece(s) of glassware has/have the greatest **precision** for measuring volume: the 10.00-mL graduated cylinder, 50.0-mL graduated cylinder, 50.00-mL buret or 10.00-mL pipet? (Refer to the instructions above for answering this question.)

3. Which piece of glassware would you use if the volume of liquid needed be measured relatively quickly and did not need to be extremely precise? Explain your reasoning.

4. Which of these pieces of glassware would be best to deliver a precise volume into a solution but you do not know ahead of time what that volume would be? Explain your reasoning.

LAB REPORTS

Complete the report form neatly **using ink**. Use appropriate significant figures and include units. Partners must take turns filling out sections of the worksheet. The report form is due at the end of the lab period.

LAB NOTES

Each person must turn in the duplicate copies of their lab notebook pages containing all of the raw data and observations from the lab at the end of the lab period.

Title: _____

Work Done and Report Prepared by: _____

Date: _____ Lab Section Number: _____

GOAL

DATA

Practice Using Graduated Cylinders

10.00 mL Graduated Cylinder

Mass of 125-mL Erlenmeyer flask (g) _____

Table 1. Practice Using a 10.00 mL Graduated Cylinder *(use proper significant figures)*

Trial	Total Measured Volume (mL)	Total Mass (g)	Mass of deionized water (g)	Calculated Density (g/mL)
1				
2				
3				

Temperature of deionized water (°C) = _____

50.0 mL Graduated Cylinder

Mass of 125-mL Erlenmeyer flask (g) _____

Table 2. *Practice Using a 50.00 mL Graduated Cylinders (use proper significant figures)*

Trial	Total Measured Volume (mL)	Total Mass (g)	Mass of deionized water (g)	Calculated Density (g/mL)
1				
2				
3				

Temperature of deionized water (°C) = _____

Practice Using a Buret

Mass of 125-mL Erlenmeyer flask (g) _____

Table 3. Practice Using a Buret *(use proper significant figures)*

Trial	Total Measured Volume (mL)	Total Mass (g)	Mass of deionized water (g)	Calculated Density (g/mL)
1				
2				
3				

Temperature of deionized water (°C) = _____

Practice Using a Pipet

Mass of 125-mL Erlenmeyer flask (g) _____

Table 4. Practice Using a Pipet *(use proper significant figures)*

Trial	Total Measured Volume (mL)	Total Mass (g)	Mass of deionized water (g)	Calculated Density (g/mL)
1				
2				
3				

Temperature of deionized water (°C) = _____

DATA ANALYSIS

Table 5. Graduated Cylinder Calculation Results

Theoretical density of water at _____ °C = _____ (10.00 mL graduated cylinder)

Theoretical density of water at _____ °C = _____ (50.00 mL graduated cylinder)

	Trial	Calculated Density* (g/mL)	Abs Dev $\lvert x_i - \bar{x} \rvert$ ** (g/mL)	% error***
10.00-mL graduated cylinder	1			
	2			
	3			
	Average			
50.0-mL graduated cylinder	1			
	2			
	3			
	Average			

*transfer your results from Tables 1 and 2

**absolute difference between the individual measurement (x_i) and the average ($\bar{x}$)

***see equation (2)

Sample calculation of the absolute deviation ($|x_i - \bar{x}|$) and percent error for Trial # _____ using the 50.0-mL graduated cylinder:

(Show your work and label units.)

Table 6. Buret Calculation Results

Theoretical density of water at _____ °C = _____

Trial	Calculated Density* (g/mL)	Abs Dev $|x_i - \bar{x}|$ ** (g/mL)	% error***
1			
2			
3			
Average			

Table 7. Pipet Calculation Results

Theoretical density of water at _____ °C = _____

Trial	Calculated Density* (g/mL)	Abs Dev $|x_i - \bar{x}|$ ** (g/mL)	% error***
1			
2			
3			
Average			

*transfer your results from Table 3 or 4

**absolute difference between the individual measurement (x_i) and the average ($\bar{x}$)

***see equation (2)

Table 8. Summary of Results

Glassware	Temp of water, °C	Average Calculated Density, g/mL	Mean Absolute Deviation (MAD)* $\dfrac{\sum |x_i - \bar{x}|}{n}$	Average Percent Error*
10.00-mL graduated cylinder				
50.0-mL graduated cylinder				
50.00 mL buret				
10.00 mL pipet				

*transfer results from bold outlined cells in Tables 5, 6 and 7

DISCUSSION

Using complete sentences, answers the questions found in the lab manual. Use reverse or additional paper if needed.

CHAPTER 3

HOW CAN WE USE A PHYSICAL PROPERTY TO DEVELOP A SEPARATION METHOD?[1]

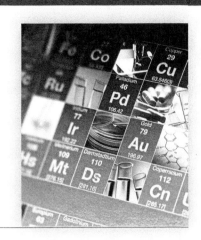

INTRODUCTION

Density is the amount of mass per unit of volume, or the mass divided by the volume (density = mass/volume). Density is an intrinsic property of a substance, meaning the density is the same no matter how much of the substance is present. The mass and the volume of a substance are proportional to each other, thus the value of the density remains the same when you change the amount of substance present.

The density of a liquid depends on the temperature of the liquid and the concentration of any substances dissolved in the liquid (solutes). Pure water has a density of about 1.0 g/mL at 4 °C. The density of water decreases as the temperature increases. Dissolving salt in water often increases the density of the solution because the overall mass of the solution increases without much change in the volume. For example, a saturated sodium chloride solution has a density of about 1.2 g/mL.

To determine the density of an object, you need to find the mass and the volume of the object. In lab, we find the mass of an object using an analytical balance. One of the simplest ways to measure the volume of an object is by liquid displacement. If the object completely sinks in the liquid, then the volume of the object is equal to the amount of liquid it displaces. If the object floats in the liquid, then it will NOT displace a volume of liquid equal to its volume since a portion of the object is above the liquid. In this case the density cannot be determined by liquid displacement.

Your first task in this exercise is to explore how density is related to sinking and floating as you determine the density of several objects using deionized water and ethanol. You will then compare your experimental densities to known densities (see Table 3.1 below) and calculate the % error of each density result.

Table 3.1. Known Density of Various Objects

Object	Density (g/mL)
Aluminum	2.70
Poplar wood	0.455
Polypropylene	0.946
Rubber	1.10

1   Adapted from "Are You Dense or What?" by Dr. Eric Malina, Department of Chemistry, University of Nebraska-Lincoln.

Your second task is to separate 6 types of recyclable plastics into the individual types using the physical property of density. You will experiment with samples of the 6 plastics and 3 liquids (100% ethanol, 4 M calcium chloride solution and deionized water) to develop a separation method. Then you will write a brief but detailed description of how you separated the plastics. Finally, you will write a step-by-step procedure for separating the six types of plastics that someone unfamiliar with the task could use to reproduce your work.

Table 3.2. Six types of plastic to be separated

Type of plastic	Abbreviation	Recycling Code ♻
high density polyethylene	HDPE	2
low density polyethylene	LDPE	4
polyester	PET	1
polypropylene	PP	5
polystyrene	PS	6
polyvinyl chloride	PVC	3

PROCEDURE

Perform this experiment in groups of 2 (pairs), with each person practicing each of the techniques. Each person must record a complete set of data in her/his lab notebook pages. **The laboratory notebook is where you record everything you do, observe and measure while in lab. It is not a full report and does NOT need to include calculations, results and discussion.**

SAFETY

Ethanol (100%) is extremely flammable. No flames are allowed in the laboratory.

Use a student bench hood when working with ethanol. The student bench hoods are found in the cabinets below the main hoods. Your TA will demonstrate proper use of the student bench hood.

All ethanol solutions must be discarded in the waste jar in the main hood.

Note: Your group is limited to 50 mL of 100% ethanol and 30 mL of 4 M $CaCl_2$ solution for the *entire experiment*, so you will need to reuse these solutions for several measurements.

PART A: DENSITY: SINKING AND FLOATING

Obtain samples of aluminum (Al), poplar wood, polypropylene, and rubber from the reagent bench.

Make sure that each object is completely dry. Measure and record the mass (g) of each object. Use the same balance for each of your measurements.

Density Determination with Deionized Water

Determine the volume (mL) of each object by water displacement, if possible, using the following process.

1. Select the smallest graduated cylinder that will still allow the objects to fit in the cylinder.

2. Add enough water to the cylinder to allow the object to submerge completely and still have a total volume less than the maximum capacity of the cylinder.

3. Record the volume of the water BEFORE you add the object to the cylinder. Pay attention to appropriate significant figures.

4. **Carefully add the object to the cylinder**, avoiding any splashing. *Be careful because metal objects dropped into the cylinder directly can crack the cylinder.*

5. Record the total volume of the water and the object. Pay attention to appropriate significant figures.If the object floats, then record "floats" for the final volume in the data table.

Calculate the volume of each object, if possible.

Calculate the density of each object, if possible. Record your results using the appropriate number of significant figures.

Density Determination with 100% Ethanol

Repeat the procedure with 100% ethanol and record the volume displaced by each object, if possible. You are limited to 50 mL of ethanol for this task and the next, so you must reuse the ethanol and save it for the next task. (The density of 100% ethanol is 0.79 g/mL at room temperature.)

▶ **Use a student bench hood when working with 100% ethanol.**

Calculate the density of each object, if possible. Record your results using the appropriate number of significant figures.

RESULTS AND DISCUSSION

Calculate the percent error for the density you determined for each of the objects based on volume displacement in water and in ethanol.

Answer the questions below, neatly and in complete sentences, on your lab report form.

How do your density results for aluminum, wood, polypropylene and rubber compare with the known values? Support your claims with experimental evidence, including your % error results. Suggest changes that could be made to improve your results.

Use your density results from the first part of this lab to write a **general** guideline that can be used to determine if an object will sink or float in a particular liquid. Your guideline could be in the form "if *xyz*, then the object will float. If *abc*, then the object will sink."

PART B: SOLVE THE PLASTICS PROBLEMS

Your task is to design a method in which you can separate a mixture of six types of plastic (types that are typically recycled) using the physical property of density. Your separation procedure should be applicable and practical on an industrial scale (i.e. visually separating the pieces is NOT a practical solution).

Available materials:

- Samples of each type of plastic
- 100% ethanol (density = 0.79 g/mL at room temperature); reused from previous section
- 4 M calcium chloride ($CaCl_2$) solution (density = 1.3 g/mL)
- deionized water.

To test your procedure in lab, your mixture should contain one piece of each type of plastic. Recall that you are limited to 50 mL of ethanol and 30 mL of $CaCl_2$ solution for the entire experiment.

▶ **Use a student bench hood when working with 100% ethanol.**

Develop a procedure for separating the six types of plastic.

RESULTS AND DISCUSSION

Answer the questions below, neatly and in complete sentences, on your lab report form.

Describe the process or method you used to develop a procedure to separate the different types of plastic. What techniques did you try? How did you manipulate densities of the liquids? Describe your process clearly and in detail.

Write step-by-step instructions for your procedure to separate the six types of plastics. Provide enough detail that someone could repeat your exact procedure by following the instructions. Your procedure can either use relative volumes ("parts") or actual volume measurements. Indicate which type of plastic is separated in each step of the procedure or list the plastics in order of their separation by density.

CLEAN UP AND WASTE DISPOSAL

All ethanol solutions must be discarded in the waste jar in the main hood.

Calcium chloride solutions can be disposed down the drain with lots of water.

Dry all the objects and plastic pieces and return them to the proper jar or to your instructor.

Rinse all glassware with deionized water.

Return the student bench hoods to the cabinets below the main hoods.

Lock your drawer before leaving the lab.

LAB REPORTS

Complete the report form neatly **using ink**. Use appropriate significant figures and include units. Partners must take turns filling out sections of the worksheet. The report form is due at the end of the lab period.

LAB NOTES

Each person must turn in the duplicate copies of their lab notebook pages containing all of the raw data and observations from the lab at the end of the lab period.

Title: _____

Work Done and Report Prepared by: _____

Date: _____ Lab Section Number: _____

GOALS

PART A: DENSITY

Table 1. Density Determined with Deionized Water

Object	Mass (g)	Initial Volume (mL)	Final Volume (mL)	Volume Displaced (mL)	Density (g/mL)
Aluminum					
Poplar					
Polypropylene					
Rubber					

Table 2. Density Determined with 100% Ethanol

Object	Mass (g)	Initial Volume (mL)	Final Volume (mL)	Volume Displaced (mL)	Density (g/mL)
Aluminum					
Poplar					
Polypropylene					
Rubber					

DATA ANALYSIS

Table 3. Percent Error in Density of Objects

Object	deionized water		ethanol	
	Density (g/mL)	% error	Density (g/mL)	% error
Aluminum				
Poplar				
Polypropylene				
Rubber				

Sample calculation of the percent error for the density of _____ (object) in _____ (liquid):
(Show your work and label units.)

DISCUSSION

Using complete sentences, answer the questions on lab manual p. 36.

PART B: SOLVE THE PLASTICS PROBLEM

RESULTS AND DISCUSSION

Using complete sentences, answer the questions on lab manual pp. 36-37. Attached additional paper if needed.

CHAPTER 4

HOW CAN THREE SMALL MOLECULES BE USED TO SYNTHESIZE A CALCIUM CHANNEL BLOCKER?

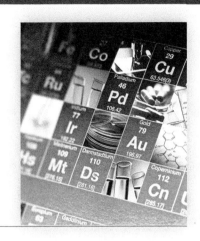

PURPOSE

The purpose of this experiment is to synthesize a calcium channel blocker by using three, small organic molecules.

INTRODUCTION

Organic compounds are molecules containing carbon atoms bonded to other carbon or hydrogen atoms and sometimes bonded to other elements, such as nitrogen. Organic synthesis is a process whereby organic molecules react with other organic molecules or reagents to form products that are different from the starting materials. Using organic synthesis, small molecules can be transformed into larger molecules, products not found in nature can be prepared, and natural products can be produced or modified. Organic synthesis is used to produce many pharmaceutically active compounds.

In organic chemistry, different groups of atoms occurring together are known as functional groups. These groups are significant because they are responsible for the chemical reactivity of a molecule. Functional groups usually react in characteristic ways, regardless of the molecule in which they are located.

The functional groups you will encounter in this experiment are shown below, both in condensed form and in carbon-skeleton form. In the carbon-skeleton form, each bend or end of a line represents a carbon atom. Hydrogen atoms are implied. (Remember that each carbon atom usually forms 4 bonds.) Note that the symbols, "R_1", "R_2" and "R_3" (i.e., "R groups") are used to represent a *group of atoms* containing at least one carbon atom. (The covalent bond to an "R group" is always to one of the carbon atoms of the "R group.")

Functional Group	Condensed Formula	Skeleton Formula
Aldehyde	$R-\overset{\overset{\displaystyle O}{\|\|}}{C}-H$	skeleton structure
Ester	$R_1-\overset{\overset{\displaystyle O}{\|\|}}{C}-O-R_2$	skeleton structure
Amide	$-\overset{\overset{\displaystyle O}{\|\|}}{C}-NH_2$	skeleton structure
Ketone	$R_1-\overset{\overset{\displaystyle O}{\|\|}}{C}-R_2$	skeleton structure

In organic chemistry, reactions in which multiple transformations occur is quite common. A classic example of such a process is the Biginelli reaction, in which an aldehyde, a β-keto ester (a compound with both ketone and ester functional groups separated by one carbon) and urea (an amide with two $-NH_2$ (amine) groups attached to the carbonyl (C=O) carbon) are combined in one pot to synthesize a 3,4-dihydropyrimidinone, as shown below. Note that the starting materials react in a 1:1:1 ratio.

$$\text{aldehyde} + \beta\text{-keto ester} + \text{urea} \xrightarrow{H^+} \text{3,4-dihydropyrimadinone} + 2\,H_2O \qquad (1)$$

The Biginelli reaction produces a 3,4-dihydropyrimidinone, an example of a class of compounds that exhibit pharmacological activity. Recently, 4-aryl-dihydropyrimidinones have been recognized as a new class of calcium channel blockers. Several biologically active marine alkaloids with the Biginelli product "core" have also been isolated. Calcium channel blockers are popular antihypertensives that inhibit the movement and binding of calcium ions, which leads to a relaxation of vascular smooth muscle and reduction of vascular resistance.

Reaction Mechanism

As mentioned above, the Biginelli reaction consists of multiple transformations that occur in a sequence of steps. Although the mechanism has been debated for a number of years, most researchers now agree on the one proposed by Kapp, below.

First, a rate-determining protonated imine formation takes place to produce **1**; then this species reacts with the enol form of the β-keto ester to form the ureide **2**. The final step is the cyclization, with concomitant loss of water.

Synthetic Methodology

In this experiment, you will synthesize a calcium channel blocker via a Biginelli reaction by combining benzaldehyde (the aldehyde; density = 1.05 g/mL), ethyl acetoacetate (the β-keto ester; density = 1.021 g/mL) and urea. Refer back to the equation (1) on p. 44 for the general form of the Biginelli reaction and note that in your experiment, R_1 is a phenyl group (C_6H_5), R_2 is a methyl group (CH_3) and R_3 is an ethyl group (CH_2CH_3), as shown below. You will *reflux* the reactants in ethanol (the solvent).

Approximately 80% of organic reactions involve a step called *reflux*. When a reaction mixture is refluxed, a solvent is used to keep substances dissolved and at a constant temperature by boiling the solvent, condensing it, and returning it to the reaction flask. Thus, reflux can be used for reactions that must be kept at a relatively constant temperature (i.e., near the boiling point of the *solvent*) for a long period of time.

$R_1 = C_6H_5$

benzaldehyde ethyl acetoacetate urea

$R_2 = CH_3$ $R_3 = CH_2CH_3$

Reporting Yield

Chemists typically report the results of a synthetic process in terms of the *percent yield* of the product. To calculate the percent yield, the *actual* and *theoretical yields* are needed. The actual yield is determined by weighing the dried solid product. The theoretical yield is calculated based on the balanced chemical equation and the mass of *limiting reactant*, which is the reactant that is completely consumed in the reaction.

In this experiment, you must determine which of the reactants (benzaldehyde, ethyl acetoacetate or urea) is the limiting reactant. Then you will use the mass of the limiting reactant, the molar masses of the limiting reactant and the product, and the molar ratios in the balanced chemical equation to calculate the theoretical yield. Using the mass of the product you obtain, you will calculate the percent yield of the synthesis. Refer to Section 3.4 in your textbook for more information.

PROCEDURE

SAFETY

Benzaldehyde and ethyl acetoacetate are severe irritants. These reagents are toxic if inhaled or ingested.

Concentrated (12 M) hydrochloric acid is corrosive. This concentrated acid will burn your skin and destroy clothing.

Ethanol is flammable.

You must wear gloves. If you need to leave the lab, you should remove your gloves so that you do not transport hazardous materials into the hallways.

Perform the reaction in a student bench hood. The student bench hoods are located in the cabinets under the main hoods.

PART 1: RUNNING THE REACTION

1. Set up a student bench hood against one of the bench ventilation ducts and verify that it is working properly by placing a KimWipe near the upper or lower vent inside the bench hood. The tissue will be pulled in the direction of the exhaust. If you do not detect any exhaust, notify your TA.

2. Obtain a clean and dry 125-mL Erlenmeyer flask, a stir bar, 2-3 boiling chips, a hotplate, two utility clamps and a condenser with rubber tubing attached.

3. Add the stir bar and 2-3 boiling chips to the flask. The addition of boiling chips will help prevent bumping (rapid boiling that can cause the mixture to erupt from the flask).

4. Weigh between 0.7 and 0.75 g of urea into a weighing cup on a milligram balance. Record the exact mass to 3 significant figures (±0.001 g). Transfer the urea to the 125-mL flask.

5. Measure 1.3 mL of benzaldehyde into a 10-mL graduated cylinder and add to the 125-mL flask.

6. In the same graduated cylinder, measure 2.4 mL of ethyl acetoacetate and add to the flask.

7. Finally, measure 5.0 mL of 100% ethanol in the same graduated cylinder and add it to the flask as well. Record the physical appearance of the reaction mixture.

8. Take the flask to the bottle of concentrated HCl in one of the main hoods. Use the pipet provided to add 10 drops of concentrated HCl to the 125-mL flask. Record the physical appearance of the reaction mixture.

9. Use Figure 4.1 as a guide to set up the reaction apparatus, which must be assembled in front of the bench hood. Clamp the flask to a ring stand and position the flask in the middle of the hot plate. Wet the rubber stopper with some deionized water and insert it into the top of the flask. Clamp the condenser as shown. Connect the rubber tubing on the *bottom* of the condenser ("water in") to the middle water faucet. Extend the top rubber tubing ("water out") so that it reaches into the sink. Adjust the water flow to a gentle stream (if the flow is too high, the rubber tubing may blow off). Although the reaction apparatus is too tall to fit completely into the bench hood, place it as far inside your bench hood as possible.

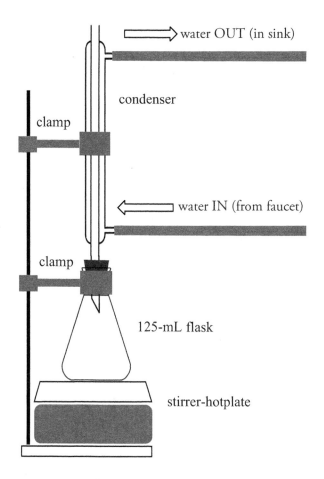

Figure 4.1. Reaction apparatus setup

10. Begin stirring the reaction mixture with a stir speed of at least 6.

11. Begin heating the reaction mixture with a heat setting of 4.

12. Continue to heat until you see ethanol dripping from the end of the condenser (refluxing). Record the time. Maintain a gentle boil, with minimal splashing. The refluxing ethanol should condense *less than half way up* the condenser. Lower the heat setting if necessary. You may also need to increase the stir rate to keep the reflux at the appropriate level.

13. Monitor the reaction for 30 minutes from when the reflux *begins* (**not** when you turn on the heat). Record any changes in the reaction mixture as the reaction progresses.

PART 2: ISOLATING THE REACTION PRODUCT

1. After 30 minutes of heating the reaction at reflux, turn off the hotplate and the water. Record the physical appearance of the reaction mixture.

2. Prepare an ice-water bath by filling a 600-mL beaker half full of ice, and adding enough water to reach the 300 mL mark on the beaker.

3. **Make sure the clamps around the flask and condenser are secure.** Carefully slide the hotplate out from under the flask. (Caution—the hot plate does not look hot, but it is hot)

4. Place the ice bath under the flask. Lower just the flask into the ice-water bath. Allow the solution to cool for 5 minutes. Record the physical appearance of the reaction mixture.

5. Remove the condenser.

6. Use Figure 4.2 as a guide to set up a vacuum filtration apparatus to separate the solid product from the solution. You will need a ring stand, 3-prong clamp, filter flask, Büchner funnel, rubber vacuum adapter, filter paper, thick-walled rubber tubing, and a plastic bucket.

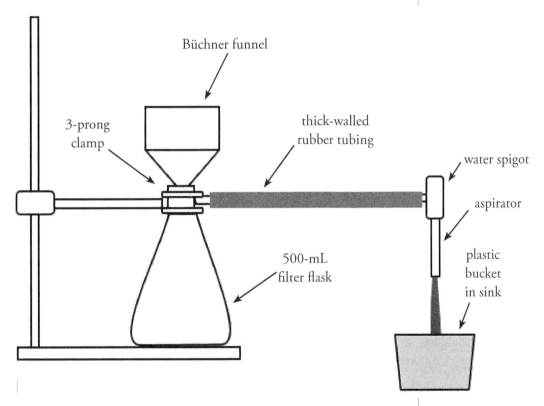

Figure 4.2. Vacuum filtration apparatus

a. Clamp the filter flask securely to a ring stand with a 3-prong clamp.

b. Check the rubber tubing to make sure it is not cracked or extremely dry. Connect the rubber tubing to the flask and the side valve on the aspirator, which is a water spigot in your sink. Place a bucket in the sink under the aspirator and fill the bucket with water.

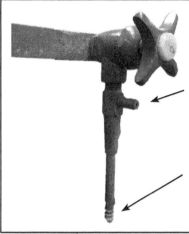

Attach one end of your rubber tubing to this nozzle; attach the other end to the side arm of the Büchner funnel. (Note: the nozzle on your aspirator may face a different direction.)

Put a plastic bucket in the sick under this spout and fill it with water. When you turn on the aspirator, this will keep water from splattering all over the bench top.

Figure 4.3. Vacuum Aspirator

c. Insert a Büchner funnel into the top of the filter flask with a rubber funnel adapter.

d. Place the filter paper in the funnel.

e. Wet the filter paper with a few milliliters of ethanol.

f. Turn on the water for the aspirator. The vacuum generated by the aspirator should draw the wet filter paper against the bottom of the funnel, sealing the bottom. Note that you may need to gently push down on the Büchner funnel while filtering to get a good vacuum. You may also need to add a second rubber adapter. Ask your TA for help.

g. Carefully pour the reaction mixture into the center of the filter paper. The vacuum should pull the liquid (called the filtrate) through the filter paper into the filter flask, leaving the solid on the filter paper. Record the appearance of the solid product.

h. Rinse the reaction flask three times with 2-mL portions of ethanol, pouring the rinses over the solid in the Büchner funnel. Record the appearance of the rinsed solid product.

i. Continue to pull a vacuum on the flask for 15 more minutes. This will draw air through the solid, which helps to dry the product.

7. Disconnect the rubber tubing from the flask, then turn off the water flow to the aspirator.

8. Record the weight of a clean, dry watch glass.

9. Remove the stir bar and boiling chips from the solid product. Use a spatula to scrape the solid product from the filter paper onto the pre-weighed watch glass.

10. Record the weight of the watch glass plus product.

WASTE DISPOSAL

Dispose of the filtrate from the vacuum filtration, excess reagents, and first rinses of the glassware in the **LIQUID WASTE** container.

Dispose the solid product in the **PRODUCT WASTE** container

Dispose the filter paper in the **FILTER PAPER WASTE** container.

CLEAN-UP

Rinse the Büchner funnel, condenser, reaction flask and filter flask with a small amount of acetone and dispose of rinse in the Liquid Waste container.

Wash the condenser, filter flask and Büchner funnel with soap and water, then rinse them with deionized water. Return them to the drawers/cabinets in the back of the room.

Allow the hotplate to cool. Remove the power cord and return the plate and cord to the side bench.

Return the student bench hood to a cabinet under one of the main hoods.

Return the bucket and vacuum tubing to the back of the room.

Clean the stir bar and return it to the TA.

DATA ANALYSIS/CALCULATIONS

Determine the limiting reagent in the reaction and calculate the theoretical yield of the 3,4-dihydropyrimidinone product.

Calculate the actual yield and the percent yield of your product.

DISCUSSION

1. Why is the solution cooled prior to crystallization? Explain your reasoning.

2. What is the purpose of washing the solid product with ethanol? Explain your reasoning.

3. Identify possible sources of error to explain why your percent yield result might vary from 100%. State at least one reason the yield might be higher than 100% and at least one reason the yield might be lower than 100%.

LAB RECORDS AND REPORTS

Group Portion

You and your partner or group will turn in one completed report, either a formal lab report or a completed lab report form at the end of this chapter.

It is your responsibility as a group to ensure that everyone whose name is on the report has participated as fully as possible in the completion of the project.

The report or report form is an organized summary of your work and does not replace the need to keep a complete set of lab or field notes in your lab notebook as the lab is being done and data collected.

Individual Portion

Each student must attach laboratory notebook duplicate pages containing a complete data set and observations for the experiment.

Title: _____

Work Done and Report Prepared by: _____

Date: _____ Lab Section Number: _____

GOAL

DATA

Reaction equation:

(Draw structural formulas (expanded, condensed or skeleton), including the specific "R" groups for the reaction you performed.)

Table 1. Reagents *(Use appropriate significant figures)*

Name	Amount (volume or mass)

Observations/Details about the preparation process:

Physical description of reaction mixture before and after addition of HCl, but before heating:

Physical description(s) of reaction mixture during heating:

Physical description of reaction mixture after 30 minutes of reflux:

Physical description of product after initial vacuum filtration:

Physical description of final isolated product:

Mass of watch glass = _____

Mass of watch glass and product = _____

Mass of product = _____

Description of product:

DATA ANALYSIS

Limiting reactant: _____
(show calculation/work below)

Theoretical yield of product (based on actual amount of limiting reactant used) = _____
(show calculation/work below)

RESULTS

Actual yield of our product = _____

Percent yield of our product = _____
(show calculation/work below)

DISCUSSION

Answer the questions found in the lab instructions. Use the reverse if necessary.

CHAPTER 5

HOW CAN WE USE CHEMICAL INTERACTIONS TO CHARACTERIZE COMPOUNDS?

This experiment will use simple observations about the behavior of acids, bases, and salts to identify an unknown solution.

GOALS

- Write simple ionic equations.
- Record observations accurately.
- Deduce identity of unknowns based upon observations.
- Support identity based upon experimental evidence.
- Communicate results clearly in complete paragraphs.

INTRODUCTION

Textbook

To be successful in the experiment, you will need to read and/or review the following topics in your textbook (use the Table of Contents or Index to find the specific pages):

- Ionic and covalent compounds (Section 2.7)
- Charges of monoatomic ions (2.8)
- Common polyatomic ions and their charges (2.8)
- Aqueous solutions of ions (4.1)
- Net ionic equations (4.2)
- Precipitation reactions and solubility rules (4.3)
- Acid-base reactions; strong and weak acids and bases (4.4)
- Gas-forming reactions: acids with carbonates (4.4)

OBSERVATIONS

The keys to success in this experiment are observation and deduction. You must be able to carefully observe what happens when two reagents are mixed and deduce from these observations what ions might be present in the unknown sample. You will observe the following characteristics:

- color

- pH

- evolution of gas upon reaction with a reagent

- formation of a precipitate (and precipitate color) upon reaction with a reagent

- lack of formation of a precipitate upon reaction with a reagent

To help you interpret your observations, keep the following general principles in mind.

Color

Solutions of certain metal ions have characteristic colors:

$Ni^{2+}(aq)$ ion is green

$Cu^{2+}(aq)$ is blue

$Fe^{3+}(aq)$ is often yellow-orange.

The precipitates that form when two solutions are mixed may also have characteristic colors, which can help identify the unknown. The colors of certain common insoluble salts are given in a table at the end of this experiment. For example, a black precipitate indicates the presence of the S^{2-} ion **and** the presence of one of the following: Ag^+, Fe^{3+}, Ni^{2+}, Cu^{2+}, Hg^{2+}, and Pb^{2+}. Other tests are necessary to determine the identity of the positive ion.

Acidity/Basicity

Whether an unknown solution is acidic or basic can be determined with the pH paper in your laboratory drawer. To test the pH of a solution, dip a clean glass stirring rod into the solution and touch the end of the glass rod to a piece of the pH paper. (The pH paper can be conserved by tearing a single strip of the pH paper into 5 pieces, and using one piece for each unknown solution.) Acidic solutions have a pH below 7; basic solutions have a pH above 7. Acids and bases can be classified as strong or weak, depending on the extent to which they dissociate into ions.

Strong acids

Compounds such as HCl, HNO_3, H_2SO_4, and $HClO_4$ are strong acids. These acids dissociate completely in aqueous solution.

Weak acids

Compounds such as HF, H_3PO_4 and CH_3COOH are weak acids, which dissociate to a very limited extent.

Some salts, such as $Fe(NO_3)_3$, $FeCl_3$, $ZnSO_4$, and $Al_2(SO_4)_3$ can behave as acids. In these cases, the metal ion reacts with water to produce hydrogen ions when the salt dissolves in water. For example, Fe^{3+} ions react with water as shown in the following equation.

$$Fe^{3+}(aq) + 3\,H_2O(aq) \rightarrow Fe(OH)_3(aq) + 3\,H^+(aq)$$

In some cases, this reaction produces a solution that can be confused with a strong acid, i.e., a solution for which the pH is less than 3.

Weak bases

Ammonia (NH_3) is a common weak base. It reacts with water to produce the OH^- ion, which can then react with other ions, such as Fe^{3+}.

$$NH_3(g) + H_2O(aq) \rightarrow NH_4{}^+(aq) + OH^-(aq)$$

Many salts such as Na_2CO_3, Na_2S, and Na_3PO_4 are also basic. These salts give solutions containing the OH^- ion due to reactions of their anions with water.

$$CO_3{}^{2-}(aq) + H_2O(aq) \rightarrow HCO_3{}^-(aq) + OH^-(aq)$$

$$S^{2-}(aq) + H_2O(aq) \rightarrow HS^-(aq) + OH^-(aq)$$

$$PO_4{}^{3-}(aq) + 2\,H_2O(aq) \rightarrow H_2PO_4{}^-(aq) + 2\,OH^-(aq)$$

The reactions involving Na_2S or NH_3 can proceed to such an extent that the solution can be confused with a strong base, i.e., a solution with a pH above 11.

Strong bases

KOH, NaOH, and $Ca(OH)_2$ are all strong bases. This category includes salts that dissolve in water to liberate the OH^- ion and compounds that react with water to produce the OH^- ion.

$$Na(OH)(s) \xrightarrow{H_2O} Na^+(aq) + OH^-(aq)$$

Evolution of Gases

Unknowns that contain the carbonate ($CO_3{}^{2-}$) or bicarbonate ($HCO_3{}^-$) ions react with acidic solutions to produce carbon dioxide, which can be seen producing bubbles.

$$CO_3{}^{2-}(aq) + 2\,H^+(aq) \rightarrow H_2O(aq) + CO_2(g)$$

$$HCO_3{}^-(aq) + H^+(aq) \rightarrow H_2O(aq) + CO_2(g)$$

Solubility

A precipitate is observed whenever a compound forms that is not soluble in aqueous solution. Solubility rules usually classify a compound as "insoluble" if a precipitate forms when the ion concentrations are about 0.1 M.

For example:

0.1 M $Na^+ + 0.1$ M $Cl^- \rightarrow$ no precipitate observed, NaCl is classified as a soluble compound

0.1 M $Ag^+ + 0.1$ M $Cl^- \rightarrow$ white precipitate observed, AgCl is classified as an insoluble compound

(At lower concentrations, precipitates may not form even if they are listed as "insoluble" by the solubility rules.)

The formation of a precipitate when two solutions are mixed, coupled with the following guidelines about solubility, can help you identify your unknowns.

For example:

0.1 M ? $+ 0.1$ M $Cl^- \rightarrow$ no precipitate observed; neither Ag^+, Pb^{2+}, Hg_2^{2+}, nor Cu^+ is present

$\rightarrow$ white precipitate observed; either Ag^+, Pb^{2+}, Hg_2^{2+}, or Cu^+ is present

Table 5.1. Solubility of common ionic compounds in water

Soluble Ionic Compounds	Insoluble Exceptions
Common salts of NO_3^-	None
Common salts of Na^+, K^+, and NH_4^+	None
Common salts of Cl^-, Br^-, and I^-	Ag^+, Pb^{2+}, Hg_2^{2+}, and Cu^+ (**not** Cu^{2+}) salts
Common salts of SO_4^{2-} *Note*: Under the conditions of this experiment, $AgSO_4$ is soluble.	Ca^{2+}, Ba^{2+}, Sr^{2+}, and Pb^{2+} salts
Common compounds of NH_4^+ For example, AgCl is soluble in $NH_3(aq)$. $AgCl(s) + 2\ NH_3(aq) \rightarrow Ag(NH_3)^{2+}(aq) + Cl^-(aq)$	None

Table 5.2. Insoluble ionic compounds in water

Insoluble Ionic Compounds	Soluble Exceptions
Common salts of S^{2-}	Na^+, K^+, NH_4^+, Ba^{2+}, and Ca^{2+} salts
Common metal hydroxides (OH^-)	Group 1A(1) hydroxides (alkali metal hydroxides) and $Ca(OH)_2$, $Sr(OH)_2$, and $Ba(OH)_2$
Common carbonates (CO_3^{2-})	Carbonates of Group 1A(1) and NH_4^+

Colors of Common Insoluble Salts

Precipitates often have characteristic colors which can be used to help identify the ions present. Refer to Table 5.3.

Table 5.3. Colors of common insoluble salts

Colors of Common Insoluble Salts	
Chlorides, Cl^-	
$AgCl$ = white	Hg_2Cl_2 = white
$PbCl_2$ = white	$CuCl$ = white
Iodides, I^-	
AgI = yellow	Hg_2I_2 = yellow to orange-red
PbI_2 = bright yellow	CuI = brown
Sulfates, SO_4^{2-}	
$BaSO_4$ = white	$PbSO_4$ = white
Sulfides, S^{2-}	
Ag_2S = black	CuS = black
Fe_2S_3 = black	HgS = black
NiS = black	PbS = black
Hydroxides, OH^-	
$AgOH$ = grey-brown	$Cu(OH)_2$ = pale blue
$Fe(OH)_3$ = rust	$Ni(OH)_2$ = pale green
$Pb(OH)_2$ = white	$Zn(OH)_2$ = white
Carbonates, CO_3^{2-}	
$CuCO_3$ = pale blue	Ag_2CO_3 = pale yellow / cream / white
$BaCO_3$ = white	$CaCO_3$ = white

PROCEDURE

Overview

The goal of this experiment is to identify each of the five unknowns assigned by your instructor. In your laboratory report you will identify each unknown, write a balanced equation for each reaction used to identify the unknown, and write a paragraph citing evidence for your identification of each unknown. Reading the preceding pages should provide you with an enormous amount of help in identifying each unknown.

Chemicals

Record the unknown numbers provided by your instructor in your data table in the report form. Please read the labels of the reagents and unknown solution bottles carefully.

One unknown will come from each of the following classes:

Class	Possible Unknowns		
Strong acid	HCl	HNO_3	H_2SO_4
Base	KOH	NH_3	Na_2S
Chloride salt	NaCl	$CuCl_2$	$BaCl_2$
Nitrate salt	$AgNO_3$	$Cu(NO_3)_2$	$Fe(NO_3)_3$
Sodium salt	NaI	Na_2SO_4	Na_2CO_3

The following reagents (aqueous solutions) will be available to identify your unknown solutions:

  (1) KOH

  (2) $AgNO_3$

  (3) $BaCl_2$

  (4) NaCl

  (5) NH_3 in water

  (6) Na_2S

  (7) Na_2SO_4

  (8) H_2SO_4

Safety

! WEAR GLOVES: If you leave the lab, take the gloves off and recycle them. Get new gloves when you return to lab.

! USE A STUDENT BENCH HOOD: The test tubes containing the unknowns and reagents, as well as the waste collection beaker, should be kept within a student bench hood to vent any gases evolved.

Never smell or sniff a chemical directly with your nose—hazardous chemicals can burn your nose and lungs or be toxic. The proper way to smell a chemical is to carefully wave your hand above the container toward your nose.

Materials

From your lab drawer, clean all your small test tubes. (The test tubes must be kept clean in order to obtain accurate results.) Set your 600 mL beaker in your student bench hood to collect waste.

Test Procedure

Lab work is done in **pairs**. Each person must record each test performed and observations in his/her laboratory notebook and turn in the duplicate copy with the laboratory report at the end of lab.

Use the following procedure for each test:

- Add **five** drops of the unknown from the labeled dropper bottle to a clean small test tube.

- Add one of the test solutions to the test tube, one drop at a time, until a total of 10–15 drops have been added. Tips of dropper bottles must not touch the solution being tested.

- Describe your observations accurately and briefly in your lab notebook.

- Clean each test tube after each test.

You might want to perform all possible tests on each of your unknowns, although it is possible to identify the unknowns without doing all the tests.

Hints

If you have difficulty differentiating between NH_3 and KOH:

Use 5 drops $AgNO_3$ + 10 drops of known NH_3

Use 5 drops $AgNO_3$ + 10 drops of known KOH

Use 5 drops $AgNO_3$ + 10 drops of unknown

The reaction of Ba^{2+} and S^{2-} may produce a cloudy white precipitate, even though according to solubility rules it shouldn't.

Waste Disposal and Cleanup

Use the 600 mL beaker stored within your student bench hood to collect chemical waste. After emptying the solutions from the test tubes into the waste collection beaker, a rinse with a few milliliters of deionized water is usually sufficient to rinse out most of the remaining waste material into the waste collection beaker. Additional rinses can be washed down the sink.

When finished, you should empty the waste collection beaker into the waste container found in the first main hood. Use a small (a few mL) rinse to transfer any remaining material into the waste container in the main hood. Additional rinses can be washed down the sink.

Return the student bench hoods to a cabinet under one of the main hoods.

Results

1. Clearly record your observations in the data table found in the report form.

2. Write a paragraph identifying each unknown (include its unknown number you recorded in the data table). You must cite evidence for each claim you make. Write in complete sentences. You should have at least one paragraph for each unknown.

3. For each unknown, write balanced net ionic equations for each reaction that you used to identify the unknown.

Helpful Information

To help you write your results paragraphs, here are examples of poor, good, and excellent writing.

Poor Paragraph

"I believe that unknown 4 is HCl(aq). There were no reactions with any reagent, so that's what I think it is."

Why is this poor? It doesn't use the color of solution or pH. It doesn't go into any detail of the experimental observations that led the student to this conclusion.

Good Paragraph

"I believe that unknown 4 is $HNO_3(aq)$. The unknown had a pH of 1, and was clear. There were no reactions with any reagent, so that's what I think it is."

Why is this good? It gives a description of the solution and its pH. But a clear solution is not necessarily colorless. It would be more complete to state that it was "clear and colorless." It doesn't go into any detail of the experimental observations that led the student to this conclusion.

Excellent Paragraph

"I believe that unknown 4 is $HNO_3(aq)$. The unknown had a pH of 1, and was a clear and colorless solution. The pH measurement indicates that it is a strong acid—HCl, HNO_3, or H_2SO_4. There were no reactions with aqueous solutions of $AgNO_3$, $BaCl_2$, NaCl, Na_2SO_4, or H_2SO_4. When Na_2S was added to the unknown an odor of rotten eggs was observed."

Why is this excellent? It gives a description of the solution and its pH. It provides clear experimental evidence of both negative tests (no reaction) and positive tests that include the student's observations. Note that the student could also have clearly identified which tests eliminated HCl(*aq*) and H$_2$SO$_4$(*aq*) as possibilities.

LAB RECORDS AND REPORTS
Group Portion

You and your partner or group will turn in one completed report, either a formal lab report or a completed lab report form at the end of this chapter. It is your responsibility as a group to ensure that everyone whose name is on the report has participated as fully as possible in the completion of the project.

The report or report form is an organized summary of your work and does not replace the need to keep a complete set of lab or field notes in your lab notebook as the lab is being done and data collected.

Individual Portion

Each student must attach laboratory notebook duplicate pages containing a complete data set and observations for the experiment.

STUDENT NOTES

Title: _____

Work Done and Report Prepared by: _____

Date: _____ Lab Section Number: _____

Table 1. Data and Observations

Unknown #					
Color					
pH					
KOH					
$AgNO_3$					
$BaCl_2$					
NaCl					
$NH_3(aq)$					
Na_2S					
Na_2SO_4					
H_2SO_4					

Unknown # _____   Unknown identity _____

Paragraph:

Balanced net ionic equations:

Unknown # _____   Unknown identity _____

Paragraph:

Balanced net ionic equations:

Unknown # _____   Unknown identity _____

Paragraph:

Balanced net ionic equations:

Unknown # _____   Unknown identity _____

Paragraph:

Balanced net ionic equations:

Unknown # _____   Unknown identity _____

Paragraph:

Balanced net ionic equations:

CHAPTER 6

HOW CAN WE PRODUCE A SALT FROM AN ELEMENT?*

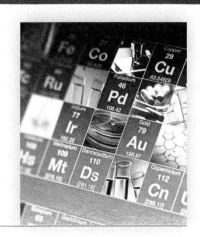

GOALS

The goals of this lab activity are to prepare and recover an inorganic compound called an alum. Alums are double sulphate salts, with the formula $AM(SO_4)_2 \cdot 12\,H_2O$, where A is a monovalent cation such as potassium, K^+, or ammonium, NH_4^+, and M is a trivalent metal ion such as aluminum, Al^{3+}, or chromium(III), Cr^{e+}. The specific alum that will be made in this experiment is the hydrated potassium aluminum sulfate with the formula $KAl(SO_4)_2 \cdot 12\,H_2O$. Alums are useful for cosmetics (astringent/blood coagulant, antiperspirant/ antibacterial), cooking (pickling/preservative), as a flame retardant, and in water treatment (causes particles to stick together and settle out of solution).

A chemical synthesis can consist of several reaction steps to transform the starting materials to the final desired product. Each reaction step will add the reagents needed to transform the original compound closer to the desired product. After each reaction step, a separation or purification step may be performed, either removing unreacted reagents or undesired side products before adding the reagents for the next step, or to recover the desired product at the end of the synthesis.

The separation and recovery steps will involve filtration and crystallization techniques.

Filtration is a separation technique usually used to separate the components of mixtures containing solids and liquids or solids and gases. Gravity filtration and vacuum filtration are commonly used in chemistry. Refer to Appendix D (Filtration) for more information.

Crystallization, or precipitation, is used to recover a solute from a solution. The technique involves decreasing the solubility of a solute in the solution to force the solute to precipitate out of the solution. This is can be done by cooling, which normally decreases the solubility of a solid. After the solid forms, filtration is used to separate the solid from the solution.

In this experiment, you will prepare the inorganic salt alum in two steps, as shown in the chemical equations below.

Step 1: $2\,Al(s) + 2\,KOH(aq) + 6\,H_2O(l) \rightarrow 3\,H_2(g) + 2\,KAl(OH)_4(aq)$

Step 2: $KAl(OH)_4(aq) + 2\,H_2SO_4(aq) + 8\,H_2O(l) \rightarrow KAl(SO_4)_2 \cdot 12\,H_2O(aq)$ (alum)

* Adapted from *Laboratory Manual to Accompany World of Chemistry,* Saunders College Publishing, 1991, Experiment 25.

The product of step 1 is an aqueous solution of $KAl(OH)_4$, which in step 2 will be treated with sulfuric acid (H_2SO_4), followed by cooling of the solution, to form solid alum, $[KAl(SO_4)_2 \cdot 12\ H_2O](s)$. Alum crystallizes as a **dodecahydrate**, which means that the solid contains 12 molecules of water per molecule of $KAl(SO_4)_2$.

Data Collection

Lab work is done in pairs. Each person must record a complete set of data in his/her laboratory notebook and turn in the duplicate copy with the summary report at the end of lab.

WEAR GLOVES: If you leave the lab, take the gloves off and recycle them. DO NOT WEAR GLOVES OUTSIDE OF THE LABORATORY. Get new gloves when you return to lab.

Step 1 - Preparation of $KAl(OH)_4$

Chemical Equation

$$2\ Al(s) + 2\ KOH(aq) + 6\ H_2O(l) \rightarrow 3\ H_2(g) + 2\ KAl(OH)_4(aq)$$

WARNING: Hydrogen gas is a very flammable product of this reaction; therefore, all the gas produced by the reaction must be drawn into the hood.

Get a student bench hood from the cabinet below the main hoods. Set this student bench hood back completely into the metal frame around the exhaust grill on the lab bench at your workstation. Check to make sure that air is being drawn through this hood before beginning your work.

- **Caution - the aluminum edges can cut your skin.** Obtain a piece of aluminum slightly more than 0.5 g. Prepare the metal by rubbing the surface several times with steel wool to remove any surface contamination. Wipe the aluminum surface with a KimWipe to remove any dust. Cut the cleaned aluminum into small pieces (about 1–2 cm in size) using scissors.

- Weigh the pieces of aluminum on a milligram balance on the side bench in the lab. Record the mass to ±0.001 g. **Put any excess aluminum pieces into the "Excess Aluminum" waste container.**

- Inside the student bench hood set up a hot plate. Set up a ring stand and clamp to stabilize the 100-mL beaker you will use for the reaction.

- Put the cleaned, cut, and weighed aluminum into the 100-mL beaker and place the beaker on top of the hot plate in the student bench hood. Adjust the heat setting to "3". Add 20 mL of 2 M KOH. Caution: The reaction will generate hydrogen gas.

Heat *very gently* until the solid aluminum is dissolved. (While waiting, one of the group members can begin to set up the equipment for gravity filtration.) The dissolution should take about 10–15 minutes. It if takes longer than that, consult your instructor.

▶ **Be careful not to heat too quickly or the solution will boil over. Adjust the heat setting if necessary.**

Monitor the volume of the reaction. If the liquid's volume drops below 10 mL, add enough deionized water to bring the total volume back up to about 10 mL. After all the aluminum pieces have dissolved, the solution will be grey or tan with small black particles, which are from impurities in the aluminum. These impurities will be removed by gravity filtration.

Gravity Filtering the Mixture to Remove Insoluble Impurities

- Refer to Figure 6.1 below. Prepare a clean funnel by placing a layer of glass wool into the bottom of the cone portion. Your instructor will show you the appropriate amount of glass wool to use. You do not need to use any filter paper. Have the funnel drain into a second clean 100-mL beaker.

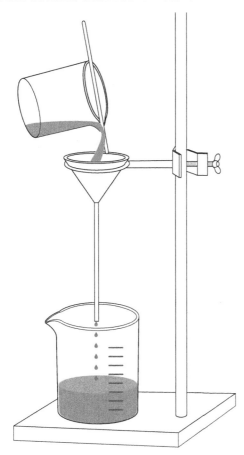

Figure 6.1. Separation technique: gravity filtration.

- Pick up the hot beaker using layers of paper towels around the beaker (DO NOT USE THE CRUCIBLE TONGS) and pour the hot reaction mixture through the glass wool in the funnel. If any significant amount of solids remain in the filtrate (the liquid in the beaker), run the filtrate through the glass wool again into another clean beaker.

- Pour 10 mL of deionized water into a clean a 100-mL beaker and heat at a setting of "3" for at least 5 minutes. With a dropper, add the 10 mL of hot deionized water drop wise to the glass wool funnel to collect any remaining reaction solution clinging to the glass wool and collect with the original filtrate. The solution may be light brown, grey, or colorless.

Put the used glass wool in the "Glass Wool Waste" container.

At this point, the solution is a mixture of K^+, $Al(OH)_4^-$ and OH^- ions.

Step 2 -Preparation of Alum, $KAl(SO_4)_2 \cdot 12 H_2O$

Chemical Equation

$KAl(OH)_4(aq) + 2 H_2SO_4(aq) + 8 H_2O(l) \rightarrow KAl(SO_4)_2 \cdot 12 H_2O(aq)$

IMPORTANT!!! Cool the aluminum solution to room temperature.

▶ **Work in the student bench hood!! Caution is needed with this step since you are adding concentrated acid to concentrated base. The solution may get sufficiently hot to spatter on you and your laboratory neighbors. Clean up any spills immediately.**

Carefully, **slowly**, and with constant stirring (use a clean glass stirring rod) add 10 mL of 9 M H_2SO_4, about 1 mL at a time, to the cooled aluminum solution. As the acid is added, "lumps" of $Al(OH)_3$ may form. By the time all of the acid has been added, most of the $Al(OH)_3$ should be dissolved.

- Heat the solution gently on the hot plate (setting of "3" again) for 5–10 minutes until the reaction mixture is clear. Then, use pH paper to check that the solution is below pH 3. If it is not, add sulfuric acid dropwise to lower the pH to 3.

Remember to clean the stirring rod; the acid can be a hazard.

If the solution is not clear at this point, filter it through glass wool as done before.

At this point, the solution is a mixture of H^+, K^+, Al^{3+} and SO_4^{2-} ions.

Recovery of Alum by Crystallization and Vacuum Filtration

Obtain a 600-mL beaker of ice.

- If the solution volume is >25 mL, heat the solution gently to reduce its volume to about 25 mL. Don't turn the hot plate higher than setting 5 or the solution may splatter or boil over, which will affect your product yield. If the solution is too dilute, you will recover less product during the crystallization.

- Use layers of paper towels to pick up the beaker and place it in a 600-mL beaker about 1/2 full of ice. Cool the solution on ice for 10–15 minutes. Stir the reaction mixture gently from time to time until fine, white crystals appear. This is the alum. (The solid may look like a powder as the crystals may be very small.)

- As the crystals form, pour 20 mL of 50% ethanol in a clean 250-mL beaker and cool in another 600-mL beaker about 1/2 full of ice. The ethanol will be used to transfer the solid remaining in the 100-mL beaker into the Büchner funnel and to rinse your crystals after filtration. The cold ethanol will help dry the alum by removing excess water from the alum, but will not dissolve the alum.

Caution - Ethanol is flammable; dispense in the main hood and keep away from hot surfaces.

▶ Refer to Appendix D (Filtration) for details about filtration methods.

- Set up a vacuum filtration apparatus as shown in Figure 6.2. Clamp the filtration flask to a ring stand using a 3-prong clamp. Put a bucket filled with water in the sink under the faucet to keep the water from splashing. Check with your TA to make sure you have the rubber tubing connected properly to the water faucet. Before you connect the tubing to the flask, open the water faucet all the way and check the strength of the vacuum by putting your finger over the open end of the tubing. Turn the water off.

- Wet the filter paper with a small amount of deionized water from your wash bottle.

- Turn the water on all the way so a vacuum is pulled on the wet filter paper. Make sure all of the holes in the Büchner funnel are covered by the filter paper so that solids cannot bypass it.

- Pour the solution containing the crystals onto the filter paper. This should be done carefully and all at once while you swirl the beaker containing the crystals.

- Use about 5 mL of the cool 50% ethanol to rinse the beaker in an attempt to pick up the remaining crystals and transfer them onto the filter paper.

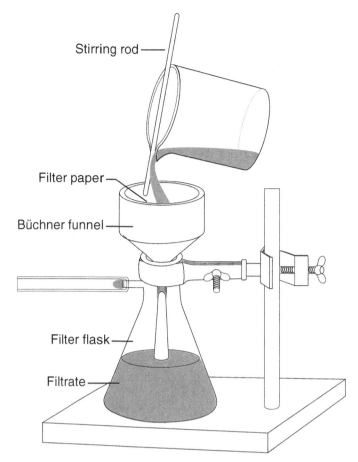

Stirring rod

Filter paper

Büchner funnel

Filter flask

Filtrate

Figure 6.2. Separation technique: suction filtration.

- Wash the crystals on the filter paper with the remaining 50% ethanol by slowly pouring the 50% ethanol over the crystals.

- Continue pulling a vacuum on the filter paper for another 15–20 minutes. If your vacuum is not strong, you may need to use a second filter adapter. Check with your lab instructor.

- While the solid is drying, begin preparing your project summary report. Leave a blank space in your lab notebook and in your report to record actual yield when the mass of alum recovered is measured. You should be able to complete all the computations except for % yield while the crystals dry.

- Weigh a clean, dry watch glass on the milligram balance to three decimal places.

- When the crystals are dry (gently prod the solid with your metal spatula, the solid should be free-flowing, fluffy—not clumpy, slushy or pasty), carefully slip the flat end of the metal spatula under the edge of the filter paper, and slide the filter paper and solid from the funnel onto a paper towel.

- Using the spoon-like end of your metal spatula, carefully scrape the alum crystals from the filter paper onto the pre-weighed watch glass. Determine the mass of alum crystals recovered to three decimal places. Describe the product. (Note that if the alum is not completely dry, the weight shown on the balance may slowly decrease due to evaporating water.)

- Clean the Büchner funnel and filter flask. Caution - the filtrate in the filter flask will contain leftover excess acid. The filtrate and rinses can be poured down the drain followed by lots of water. Filter paper is discarded in the trash can.

WASTE DISPOSAL AND CLEANUP

Rinse all glassware at least three times with distilled water.

Return all equipment to the proper storage location in the lab. The caustic nature of reagents can damage glassware if it is not clean before storing.

The solid alum you made can be rinsed down the drain followed by lots of water.

Keep your splash goggles on until you have completed and turned in the lab report, cleaned up your work area, and are leaving the lab. Lock your lab drawer before leaving lab.

Data Analysis

Calculate the theoretical yield of alum based on the amount of aluminum metal you used as starting material. You may want to refer to information in your textbook.

Results

Calculate the actual and percent yield of alum for your synthesis process.

$$\% \text{ yield} = \frac{\text{Actual Yield}}{\text{Theoretical Yield}} \times 100$$

Identify sources of error to explain your % yield result.

Discussion

1. Why is it important to reduce the volume to 25 mL or less prior to the crystallization? How will the yield of alum be affected if the volume is greater than 25 mL? Explain your reasoning.

2. Why is the solution cooled of alum prior to crystallization?

3. If your solid alum is not completely dry, how will the % yield be affected? Explain.

LAB RECORDS AND REPORTS

Group Portion

You and your partner or group will turn in one completed report, either a formal lab report or a completed lab report form at the end of this chapter.

It is your responsibility as a group to ensure that everyone whose name is on the report has participated as fully as possible in the completion of the project.

The report or report form is an organized summary of your work and does not replace the need to keep a complete set of lab or field notes in your lab notebook as the lab is being done and data collected.

Individual Portion

Each student must attach laboratory notebook duplicate pages containing a complete data set and observations for the experiment.

Title: _____

Work Done and Report Prepared by: _____

Date: _____ Lab Section Number: _____

Goal

Data

Chemical equations for the synthesis process:

The name of the starting material is _____ mass = _____

Observations/details about the preparation process:
(Note physical appearances, deviations from lab manual procedure, etc.)

The name of the product is _____ mass = _____

Description of product:

Data Analysis

Theoretical yield of product = _____

(Show calculations work in the following space.)

Results

Actual yield of our product = _____

Percent yield of our product = _____

(Show calculations work in the following space.)

Sources of error to explain % yield result:

Discussion

1. Why is it important to reduce the volume to 25 mL or less prior to the crystallization?

2. Why is the solution cooled prior to crystallization?

3. If your solid alum is not completely dry, how will the % yield be affected? Explain.

CHAPTER 7

HOW DO WE STANDARDIZE A SOLUTION?

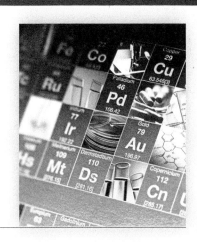

GOALS

The goals of this laboratory activity are to prepare a NaOH solution and determine the concentration of the NaOH solution accurately and precisely. This process will be based on the reaction of NaOH with a known solid acid where all reactants will be dissolved in water. The titration technique, using phenolphthalein as an indicator, will be used to obtain the necessary data for this determination. A pair of students (two students) will prepare one NaOH solution to be shared between the students as each student in the pair completes three (3) independent titrations with the NaOH solution.

INTRODUCTION

Concentration of Solutions

The mole concept can be used to determine the number of atoms, ions, or molecules in a sample of a **pure substance** by measuring the weight of the sample. Before we can extend the concept of the mole to **solutions**, we will need to know the relative amounts of the different components that make up the solution. In other words, we need to know the **concentration** of the solution. Review the information about solution stoichiometry in your textbook.

The concentration of some substances in solution can be determined and calculated precisely and accurately by careful measurements of solute mass and solution volume. Sodium hydroxide, however, absorbs atmospheric water when exposed to the atmosphere. This means that samples of sodium hydroxide normally contain an indeterminable amount of water; therefore, a measured mass value is an unreliable measurement to determine the amount of NaOH in a sample dissolved in water. To accurately determine the amount and concentration of sodium hydroxide in a solution prepared by dissolving solid NaOH in water, the process of reacting the NaOH with a known amount of acid is used. The process of using a known amount of one reagent to determine the amount or concentration of another substance is known as **standardization**.

Although there are many different units of concentration, the most commonly used unit among chemists is **molarity (M)**. Molarity is defined as the number of moles of solute per 1 L of solution. So a solution labeled 0.1234 M NaOH has 0.1234 moles of NaOH per 1 L of solution. For a solution being prepared by dissolving a solid in water, the molarity is calculated as follows:

$$M = \frac{\text{moles of solute}}{\text{liters of solution}}$$

The practicality of this concentration unit can be seen by considering how you would predict the amount of PbI_2 that could be produced by the following reaction.

$$Pb(NO_3)_2(aq) + 2\ KI(aq) \rightarrow PbI_2(s) + 2\ K^+(aq) + 2\ NO_3^-(aq)$$

Measurements of the weights of the two solutions would be useless, because they are not pure substances. One contains $Pb(NO_3)_2$ dissolved in water, while the other is a solution of KI in water. If, however, we knew the molarity of each solution—the number of moles of $Pb(NO_3)_2$ or moles of KI per liter of solution—we could measure the volume of the solutions that were mixed and calculate the number of moles of each reagent that were allowed to react. Once this is known, calculations of the amount of PbI_2 produced in this reaction are possible.

The main advantage of molarity as a unit of concentration is therefore the ease with which measurements of the volume of a solution can be combined with the molarity to determine the number of moles of the solute that are present to take part in a chemical reaction. The number of moles of solute in a given volume of solution with known concentration is calculated by multiplying the molarity by the volume.

ACID–BASE TITRATIONS

Reactions between acids and bases that are dissolved in water occur almost instantaneously; they occur as fast as the two solutions can be mixed. These reactions also tend to go to completion, reacting until all of the limiting reagent is consumed. When exact stoichiometric amounts of acid and base have been mixed, the reaction is said to have reached the **equivalence point**. Essentially all of the acid has reacted with the base, and vice versa.

The technique of slowly adding an acid to a base—or vice versa—until the reaction has reached the equivalence point is known as a **titration**.

The key to observing the equivalence point of a titration is the use of an **indicator** to indicate when the equivalence point of the reaction has been reached. Indicators take many forms. They may be as complex as an electronic probe, or as simple as the syrup of violets first described by Robert Boyle in 1661. The most familiar indicators are litmus and phenolphthalein. Litmus is a vegetable dye that is red in acid and blue in base. Phenolphthalein is colorless in acid and pink in base.

In theory, the indicator should turn color at the equivalence point. In practice, each indicator has an **endpoint**—at which it turns color—that might be slightly different from the equivalence point of the reaction. Titrations that use phenolphthalein as the indicator, for example, should be stopped just before the solution turns a permanent pink color. In this fashion, the endpoint of the indicator is brought as closely as possible to the equivalence point of the reaction.

REACTION STOICHIOMETRY

The general equation for the reaction of an acid with hydroxide is:

$$H_nA + n\,OH^- \rightarrow A^{n-} + n\,H_2O$$

where n is the number of reactive or acidic hydrogens.

The solid acids you will be using are diprotic, where n = 2.

You will use a known weight of a solid acid of known molecular weight to determine the concentration of an aqueous solution of sodium hydroxide (NaOH), using phenolphthalein as the endpoint indicator.

Because you will know both the weight of the solid acid and its molecular weight, you can calculate the number of moles of acid that are present initially. From the balanced chemical equation for the reaction, you can determine the number of moles of sodium hydroxide required to consume all of the acid. With the volume of the sodium hydroxide solution needed to reach the endpoint, you can then calculate the molarity of the NaOH solution.

Data Collection

Each pair of students will prepare one NaOH solution that is approximately 0.1 M NaOH. Each student in the pair will standardize this NaOH solution, each using a different acid.

Preparation of NaOH Solution: Prepare one solution for two students. Lab partners will share the solution.

- Refer to your prelab calculations to find the amount of NaOH you will need to prepare 250 mL of NaOH solution. *This solution will be used (shared) by two students.* You should have your graduate instructor check this number for accuracy before you begin.

- Tare a clean and dry 100-mL beaker on a milligram balance. Use your clean, dry metal spatula to carefully transfer the precalculated amount of NaOH pellets a few at a time **directly** from the reagent bottle to your tared beaker. Do not pour the NaOH pellets into a paper weighing cup or other container and then add them to your beaker, as this usually results in a lot of waste. If you do remove excess NaOH pellets, do NOT return them to the reagent bottle. Ask your TA for disposal instructions.

- The mass of NaOH does not need to match the calculated value exactly, but the mass you weigh must be recorded correctly and precisely in your notebook, using the appropriate number of digits after the decimal point (3 or 4, depending on the balance).

- Use a 100-mL graduated cylinder to measure 200 mL of deionized (DI) water into a clean 500-mL flask. Swirl to dissolve the pellets completely. When the NaOH has dissolved completely, add 50 more mL of DI water to the flask. Mix thoroughly again.

- Record how you prepared the NaOH solution in your laboratory notebook.

Preparation of Acid Solution: Done individually; each partner has a different acid (one uses oxalic acid dihydrate and one uses succinic acid).

- In your prelab assignment, you calculated the amount (in g) of solid acid required to prepare 40.0 mL of a 0.01875 M solution of the acid. Review your calculation results for the acid you are assigned to titrate. Your graduate instructor must check the value of your result for accuracy before you begin preparation of the acid solution.

- Weigh the precalculated amount of solid acid (±10%) into a clean, dry 125-mL or 250-mL Erlenmeyer flask using an analytical balance. (If your flask is wet, you may weigh the solid acid in a paper weighing cup; however, you must be sure to transfer *all* of the solid from the paper cup to the flask.)

- Be careful not to spill any of the acid. If you do, turn off the balances and clean the balance area immediately.

- You do not need to weigh the exact amount you calculated in the prelab, but you must record the exact mass weighed for each sample. Record the mass value with 3 or 4 digits after the decimal, depending on which balance you used.

- Measure approximately 40 mL of DI water using a 50.0-mL graduated cylinder and add it to the flask with the solid acid. Swirl the flask to dissolve all the acid.

- Add one to two drops of the indicator (a dilute solution of phenolphthalein in ethanol) to the acid solution.

TITRATING THE ACID WITH NaOH

Done by individual students—one partner will use oxalic acid dihydrate and the other will use succinic acid (see prelab). Each partner will perform 3 trials/titrations of the assigned acid.

In addition to being able to weigh the acid accurately, your success with this experiment will depend, to a considerable extent, on your ability to read a buret and to record the volume correctly.

▶ **Refer to Appendix B: Volumetric Measurement Techniques for detailed information about buret use.**

Titrating

- Obtain a buret from your graduate instructor. Clean it carefully with dilute soap and water. Rinse thoroughly with tap water 3–4 times followed by 3–4 rinses with DI water. Add 3–4 mL of the NaOH solution you prepared and use this solution to wet down the walls of the buret. Drain the buret and repeat the rinsing with another 3–4 mL sample of NaOH. Secure the buret in a buret clamp.

- Fill the buret with the NaOH solution you prepared to well above the 0-mL mark. Open the stopcock and rapidly drain some of the NaOH solution to remove air bubbles from the tip of the buret. Stop this procedure when the NaOH solution level is just below the 0.00 mL mark. **Record** this initial volume reading (V_i) of NaOH to **two decimal places.**

- Put an Erlenmeyer flask containing acid solution beneath the buret and place a white paper towel or piece of paper beneath the flask so that the pale pink color of the titration endpoint is clearly visible when it forms. The tip of the buret should extend into the Erlenmeyer flask to ensure that the NaOH solution does not splash onto the walls of the flask above the level that is washed down with the acid solution as the flask is swirled.

- Then add your NaOH solution (the exact concentration is unknown) to the acid solution in the flask 1 mL at a time. The Erlenmeyer flask should be swirled constantly to ensure complete mixing of reagents. As NaOH is added to the acid solution you should begin to see a pink color form on the surface of this solution. This color will fade almost instantly on swirling. When you get to the point where it seems to take longer and longer for this color to fade, slow down the titration by adding smaller amounts of NaOH each time. Refer to the prelab question in which you estimated the volume of 0.1 M NaOH solution needed to reach the equivalence point in the titration of 40.0 mL of a 0.01875 M solution of the acid. When the reaction gets within 1 mL of the endpoint, the NaOH solution should be added one drop at a time. If you are careful, you should be able to perform this experiment with a precision of plus or minus one drop of solution, or approximately 0.05 mL of solution.

- When the addition of a single drop of NaOH produces a pale pink color after the solution has been stirred, and which slowly fades over a period of about 10 seconds, the endpoint has been reached. If the solution turns to a permanent dark pink color you have gone too far! If there is any doubt about whether or not you have reached the endpoint you might read the buret, record this measurement, and add just one more drop. If one more drop produces a permanent pink color, then you have already recorded the volume of solution needed to reach the endpoint. If not, read the buret again, record this measurement, and add another drop. Repeat this procedure until the endpoint has been reached.

- **Record** the final volume reading (V_f) of the NaOH to **two decimal places**. The difference between the initial and final volume readings is the volume of NaOH solution dispensed or used to neutralize the acid.

- Repeat the weighing and titration procedure with a second and third sample of the acid.

WASTE DISPOSAL AND CLEANUP

All solutions can be poured down the drain followed by lots of water.

Rinse all glassware at least three times with deionized water. Return equipment to proper locations.

Clean the benchtop and throw paper into a large waste basket.

- **Keep your splash goggles on until you have completed and turned in the laboratory report, cleaned up your work area, and are leaving the lab.**

DATA ANALYSIS

You and your partner can consult on the data analysis, but each is responsible for their own analysis.

Write the chemical equation to represent the reaction between NaOH and the acid you used.

For each titration you did, calculate the experimental molarity of the NaOH solution you prepared.

Average the experimental molarity values that agree within the indicated limits ($\pm 1\%$).

RESULTS

In Tables 3 and 4 of the report form, report the experimental values and average you obtained for the molarity of the NaOH solution you prepared.

Comment on the precision of your results. Do they agree within the accepted limits of $\pm 1\%$? If not, why might that be? Explain your reasoning.

DISCUSSION

1. How do the results from the oxalic acid and succinic acid titrations compare? Explain. What are some reasons the results may not agree?

    ■ Compare the results of the oxalic acid titration with the estimated NaOH concentration (i.e., the concentration based on the mass of NaOH).

    ■ Compare the results of the succinic acid titration with the estimated NaOH concentration (i.e., the concentration based on the mass of NaOH).

2. Why is it necessary to use the titration technique in order to determine an accurate and precise value for the concentration of NaOH in an aqueous solution? In other words, why can't one use the mass of sodium hydroxide and the volume of the solution to determine its concentration? Explain in your own words.

LAB RECORDS AND REPORTS
Group Portion

You and your partner or group will turn in one completed report, either a formal lab report or a completed lab report form at the end of this chapter. It is your responsibility as a group to ensure that everyone whose name is on the report has participated as fully as possible in the completion of the project. The report or report form is an organized summary of your work and does not replace the need to keep a complete set of lab or field notes in your lab notebook as the lab is being done and data collected.

Individual Portion

Each student must attach laboratory notebook duplicate pages containing a complete data set and observations for the experiment.

STUDENT NOTES

Title: _____

Work Done and Report Prepared by: _____

Date: _____ Lab Section Number: _____

GOAL

Data

Preparation of NaOH solution:

    mass of NaOH: _____   volume of DI water added: _____

Estimated concentration of NaOH solution calculated using mass of NaOH and volume of deionized water: _____

Table 1. Titration Data for Oxalic acid dihydrate

Trial	Mass of acid (g)	Initial buret volume (mL)	Final buret volume (mL)

Molecular formula of acid:

Molecular weight of acid:

Reaction equation:

Stoichiometry (moles NaOH/moles acid):

Table 2. Titration Data for Succinic acid

Trial	Mass of acid (g)	Initial buret volume (mL)	Final buret volume (mL)

Molecular formula of acid:

Molecular weight of acid:

Reaction equation:

Stoichiometry (moles NaOH/moles acid):

Results

Table 3. Titration Results for Oxalic acid dihydrate

Trial	Moles of acid	Volume of NaOH delivered (mL)	Concentration of NaOH
		Average NaOH concentration =	

Sample calculation of [NaOH] for Trial #1: *(Show work and label units)*

Table 4. Titration Results for Succinic acid

Trial	Moles of acid	Volume of NaOH delivered (mL)	Concentration of NaOH
		Average NaOH concentration =	

Sample calculation of [NaOH] for Trial #1: *(Show work and label units)*

Comment on the precision of your results.

Discussion

Answer the questions found in your lab manual.

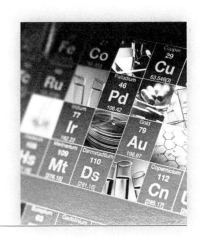

CHAPTER 8

HOW CAN ENTHALPY CHANGES FOR CHEMICAL AND PHYSICAL PROCESSES BE DETERMINED?

PURPOSE

The purposes of this experiment are to: (1) determine the enthalpy changes for the dissolution of several solid salts in water, (2) determine the enthalpy change for the reaction of 1.0 M solutions of HCl and NaOH, and (3) determine the effects of doubling the amount of a salt and of doubling the volume of HCl and/or NaOH on the enthalpy changes for these processes.

INTRODUCTION

Chemical and physical changes are accompanied by the absorption or release of energy. For example, the combustion of methane (CH_4, the major component in natural gas) is a reaction that releases energy as heat (an **exothermic** reaction).

$$CH_4(g) + O_2(g) \rightarrow CO_2(g) + H_2O(g) + heat$$

The decomposition of calcium carbonate (limestone) into carbon dioxide and calcium oxide (lime), is a reaction that absorbs heat as it proceeds (an **endothermic** reaction).

$$heat + CaCO_3(s) \rightarrow CaO(s) + CO_2(g)$$

If a reaction occurs in an insulated container, heat can neither enter the container nor escape from it.

- If an exothermic reaction is run in an insulated container, the heat produced is trapped inside the container as thermal energy and raises the temperature of the contents inside the container.

- If an endothermic reaction is run in an insulated container, the heat needed by the reaction is obtained from the thermal energy of the contents of the container. This lowers the temperature of the contents inside the container.

The amount of heat produced or absorbed by many chemical or physical processes can be measured in an insulated container (a **calorimeter**) as described in your textbook. If the amounts of the reacting substances used are known, the enthalpy change (ΔH) for the process can be determined.

In a coffee cup calorimeter, if we know the mass of the contents of the calorimeter (**mass**), the specific heat of the contents (c), and the change in temperature (ΔT), we can calculate the heat absorbed or released by the reaction.

$$q(J) = c(J/g\ K) \times \textbf{mass}(g) \times \Delta T(K) \qquad (1)$$

Remember, the solution within the calorimeter is the surroundings and the reaction is the system; therefore,

$$q_{solution} = -q_{reaction} \tag{2}$$

To find the enthalpy change of a reaction, ΔH, you will use $q_{reaction}$ divided by the number of moles of the limiting reactant.

For example, consider the reaction of 50.0 mL of 1.00 M HCl and 50.0 mL of 1.00 M NaOH.

$$NaOH(aq) + HCl(aq) \rightarrow NaCl(aq) + H_2O(l)$$

We begin by pouring 50.0 mL of 1.00 M HCl into our calorimeter. We measure the initial temperature to be 23.0 °C.

Next we pour 50.0 mL of 1.00 M NaOH into the calorimeter and stir the solution. As the reaction proceeds, the temperature of the water increases as it absorbs the energy given off by the reaction. We find the maximum temperature to be 29.7 °C.

We will assume that the density and specific heat of the acid and base to be the same as water: 1.00 g/mL and 4.18 J/g K. We calculate $q_{solution}$ as follows.

$$q_{solution} = 4.18 \text{ J/g K} \times 100.0 \text{ g} \times (29.7 - 23.0)\text{K} = 2801 \text{ J}$$

$$q_{reaction} = -q_{solution} = -2801 \text{ J}$$

To determine ΔH_{rxn}, we divide $q_{reaction}$ by the number of moles. In this reaction, we have equal moles of each reactant, and since the stoichiometry of the reaction is 1 mole HCl for each mole of NaOH, either reactant can be considered the limiting reagent:

$$0.0500 \text{ L} \times 1.00 \text{ M} = 0.0500 \text{ mol}$$

so $\Delta H_{rxn} = -2801 \text{ J}/0.0500 \text{ mol} = -5.60 \times 10^4 \text{ J/mol} = -56.0 \text{ kJ/mol}$

Additional information about calorimetry calculations can be reviewed in your textbook.

PROCEDURE

Work in groups. Each student must record a complete set of data in his/her lab notebook and turn in the duplicate copy of the data on the perforated pages from the lab notebook at the end of the lab period.

Starting *Logger Pro*

The computer must be interfaced with the *LabQuest* interface and two stainless steel temperature probes. Make sure that the computer is on and that the interface is plugged in with the USB cable. The temperature probes need to be plugged into CH1 and CH2 of the *LabQuest* interface.

Start the *Logger Pro* program. After *Logger Pro* has loaded, there will be several windows on the screen. First, in the **Graph Window**, change the scale of the y-axis to a maximum value of 40 °C. To do this, single-click on the maximum value listed on the y-axis and enter a value of 40. Then, change the minimum value listed on the y-axis to 0 °C. Next, you will need to change the time for the length of the experiment to 300 seconds. To do this, click on **Experiment** on the menu bar. Click on **Data Collection...** and then on the **Collection** tab. Enter **300** seconds for **Length**. Enter **1.0** samples/second for **Sampling Rate**. Click **Done**.

Calorimeter Constant

The coffee-cup calorimeter is not perfectly insulated—heat can be transferred between the calorimeter (the surroundings) and the solution in the calorimeter (the system). The "calorimeter constant," C_{cal}, is the amount of heat transferred between the system and the calorimeter (surroundings) per degree temperature change. Often measurement of the calorimeter constant is part of a calorimetry experiment. However, in this experiment we are going to assume that the magnitude of the calorimeter constant is negligible. In other words, we assume that no heat is transferred between the calorimeter and its contents.

Dissolution of Solid Ammonium Nitrate

With four *clean and dry* polystyrene coffee cups, construct two coffee cup calorimeters by placing one cup inside another. Measure and record the mass of each pair of coffee cups to two decimal places.

Place about 50 mL of (room temperature) deionized water in each calorimeter. Measure and record the mass of the two coffee cups *and* the deionized water to two decimal places.

Place each calorimeter inside a 600-mL beaker. Place each beaker and calorimeter on a magnetic stirrer. Put a magnetic stirring bar in each calorimeter. *Position the temperature probes toward the sides of the containers so that the stirring bars do not bump the probes as they spin.* Turn on both stirrers and adjust the stirring rates to gently stir the water.

Figure 8.1. Coffee Cup Calorimeter

Weigh out a 1.9 to 2.1 g sample of ammonium nitrate into a weighing cup and record the mass to two decimal places. Using another weighing cup, weigh out a 3.9 to 4.1 g sample of ammonium nitrate and record the mass to two decimal places.

▶ **You will need to start the data collection *before* adding the solid ammonium nitrate in order to determine the initial temperature of the water.**

Click on the **Collect** button, wait a few seconds, and then, simultaneously, transfer the 2 g sample of ammonium nitrate to one calorimeter and the 4 g sample to the second calorimeter.

Click **Stop**, ■ Stop , to end the data collection. At this time you should autoscale the graphing area to better visualize the shape of the curve representing the temperature as a function of time. Click **autoscale**, [A] . Determine the initial and final temperature from the temperature data. The final temperature will correspond to either the maximum or minimum temperature of the reaction depending on whether you are studying an exothermic or endothermic reaction. See Figure 8.2.

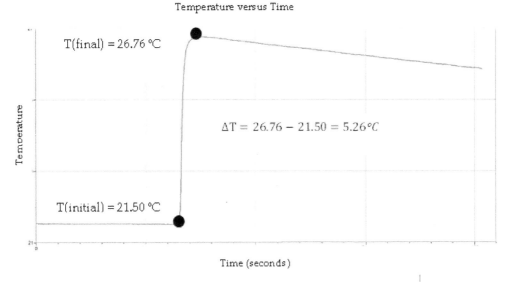

Figure 8.2. How to determine the temperature change.

PRINT GRAPHS

Plot trials using the same chemical (e.g. both trials of the dissolution of ammonium nitrate) on the same graph. To continue using the same graph, select **Store Latest** from the **Experiment** menu. The data will be stored as "Run 1" in the table. Rename "Run 1" by double clicking the "Run 1" title in the table to open the **Data Set Options** window.

You may print the graph by selecting **Print Graph** in the **File** dropdown menu. Labels and titles can be added by right-clicking on the graph area and choosing **Graph Options**. Indicate $T_{(initial)}$, $T_{(final)}$, and ΔT in writing on the printed graph. Attach the printed and labeled graph to your report form.

Repeat this procedure for the remaining experiments.

SAVE DATA

Save the data by selecting **Save As**… in the **File** menu. If you will manipulate the data with any other spreadsheet program besides Logger Pro, then export the file in a .txt format by selecting **Export As** from the **File** menu.

CLEAR DATA

You may clear the data by choosing **Clear All Data** from the **Data** menu. Make sure you have saved the data first.

▶ **All solutions can be poured down the sink.**

Dissolution of Calcium Chloride Dihydrate and Calcium Chloride Hexahydrate

Collect data for the dissolution of 2 g and 4 g samples of both calcium chloride dehydrate ($CaCl_2 \cdot 2H_2O$) and calcium chloride hexahydrate ($CaCl_2 \cdot 6H_2O$) using the same procedure described above for ammonium nitrate. Calcium chloride is hygroscopic, so keep the lids on the reagent bottles when not in use. Dispense and weigh the solid just before you are ready to add it to the calorimeter.

When the experiment is complete, save your data, print your graph, and then clear the data.

▶ **All solutions can be poured down the sink.**

Reactions of HCl and NaOH

The HCl and NaOH solutions must be measured using clean graduated cylinders. If the graduated cylinders are wet when you start the experiment, rinse each cylinder with a few mL of the appropriate solution. If you will be using more than 50 mL of the HCl or the NaOH in a particular trial, use a 100-mL graduated cylinder.

To determine the masses of the HCl solution and NaOH solution that are mixed, you will need to measure and record:

1. the mass of the coffee cup calorimeter,

2. the mass of the HCl solution initially added to the calorimeter, and

3. the total mass of the solution in the calorimeter after the reaction is complete.

You should measure (using the temperature probes) the initial temperatures of the HCl solution and the NaOH solution to be mixed in each calorimeter. *Do not mix the solutions yet!* If the temperatures of the two solutions are not within 0.5 °C of each other, warm the NaOH solution by holding the beaker/graduated cylinder in the palm of your hand, or cool the beaker/graduated cylinder in cold water.

Using two calorimeters, perform the experiments described in Table 8.1 below.

Table 8.1. Reactions of 1.0 M HCl and 1.0 M NaOH.

experiment	calorimeter #1	calorimeter #2
#1	■ place 50 mL of 1.0 M HCl in calorimeter ■ add 50 mL of 1.0 M NaOH	■ place 50 mL of 1.0 M HCl in calorimeter ■ add 100 mL of 1.0 M NaOH
#2	■ place 100 mL of 1.0 M HCl in calorimeter ■ add 50 mL of 1.0 M NaOH	■ place 100 mL of 1.0 M HCl in calorimeter ■ add 100 mL of 1.0 M NaOH

When each experiment is complete, save your data. Plot experiment #1 data on one graph and experiment #2 data on a separate graph. Print both graphs and attach them to your report form.

▶ **All solutions can be poured down the sink.**

Exiting *Logger Pro*

When you are finished with the experiments, select **Exit** from the **File** menu. A window will appear asking if you want to save changes. Click on **No**.

DATA ANALYSIS/CALCULATIONS

- Since all of the solutions are dilute, assume that they all have the same specific heat capacity as water, 4.184 J g^{-1} K^{-1}.

- Assume that the densities of water and of the solutions are 1.00 g mL^{-1}.

- Assume that the mass of solution needed for the calculations includes the mass of solute and the mass of the solvent.

- Assume that the calorimeter constant is zero (i.e. assume the calorimeter has a heat capacity of zero).

Make sure to use the proper number of significant figures when recording your calculation results.

Dissolution of Ammonium Nitrate

Calculate the enthalpy change, q_{rxn}, for the dissolution of your two samples of ammonium nitrate.

Calculate the enthalpy change, ΔH_{rxn}, for the dissolution of one mole of ammonium nitrate.

Dissolution of Calcium Chloride Dihydrate

Calculate the enthalpy change, q_{rxn}, for the dissolution of your two samples of $CaCl_2 \cdot 2H_2O$.

Calculate the enthalpy change, ΔH_{rxn}, for the dissolution of one mole of $CaCl_2 \cdot 2H_2O$.

Dissolution of Calcium Chloride Hexahydrate

Calculate the enthalpy change, q_{rxn}, for the dissolution of your two samples of $CaCl_2 \cdot 6H_2O$.

Calculate the enthalpy change, ΔH_{rxn}, for the dissolution of one mole of $CaCl_2 \cdot 6H_2O$.

Reactions of HCl and NaOH

Calculate the enthalpy changes, q_{rxn}, for the reactions of:

1. 50 mL HCl and 50 mL NaOH,
2. 50 mL HCl and 100 mL NaOH,
3. 100 mL HCl, and 50 mL NaOH, and
4. 100 mL HCl and 100 mL NaOH.

Calculate the enthalpy change, ΔH_{rxn}, for the reaction of 1.0 mole of HCl (in solution) with 1.0 mole of NaOH (in solution) from each of the measurements listed above.

RESULTS

Record your results and sample calculations on the lab report form.

DISCUSSION

1. Write chemical equations to represent the chemical or physical processes whose enthalpy changes you measured. What conclusions can you reach about the endothermic or exothermic nature of these enthalpy changes?

2. In this experiment, we assumed that the magnitude of calorimeter constant was negligible. If you had determined the value of the calorimeter constant, what would the magnitude of the calorimeter constant tell you about the insulating characteristics of a coffee-cup calorimeter? How would the calculated enthalpy changes be affected by taking into account the calorimeter constant? Explain.

3. Describe what happens when the amount of salt is doubled in the experiment. What conclusions can you draw about the relationship between the enthalpy change and the mass of the salt? Explain the reasons for your conclusions.

4. What happens when the volume of NaOH is doubled but the same volume of HCl is used in the experiment? What happens when the volumes of both HCl and NaOH are doubled in the experiment? Why?

LAB RECORDS AND REPORTS

Group Portion

You and your partner or group will turn in one completed report, either a formal lab report or a completed lab report form at the end of this chapter. It is your responsibility as a group to ensure that everyone whose name is on the report has participated as fully as possible in the completion of the project.

The report or report form is an organized summary of your work and does not replace the need to keep a complete set of lab or field notes in your lab notebook as the lab is being done and data collected.

Individual Portion

Each student must attach laboratory notebook duplicate pages containing a complete data set and observations for the experiment.

Title: _____

Work Done and Report Prepared by: _____

Date: _____ Lab Section Number: _____

GOAL(S)

DATA AND DATA ANALYSIS

Dissolution of $NH_4NO_3(s)$

Table 1. _____

Calorimeter #	NH_4NO_3, g	H_2O, g	ΔT, K	q_{soln}, J	ΔH_{rxn}, kJ/mol
1					
2					

Average ΔH_{rxn} = _____ kJ/mol

▶ Attach graph of temperature (°C) vs. time (s) for 2 samples *(title and axes labelled)*
   Label the graph to show how ΔT was determined.

Sample calculation of q_{soln} (J) for the experiment in calorimeter # _____:
(Show all work, label units and check your signs.)

Note assumption(s) used in the calculation of q_{soln}:

Sample calculation of ΔH_{rxn} (kJ/mol) for the experiment in calorimeter # _____:
(Show all work, label units and check your signs.)

Dissolution of CaCl$_2$·2H$_2$O(s)

Table 2. _____

Calorimeter #	CaCl$_2$·2H$_2$O, g	H$_2$O, g	ΔT, K	q_{soln}, J	ΔH_{rxn}, kJ/mol
1					
2					

Average ΔH_{rxn} = _____ kJ/mol

▶ Attach graph of temperature (°C) vs. time (s) for 2 samples *(title and axes labelled)*
  Label the graph to show how ΔT was determined.

Dissolution of CaCl$_2$·6H$_2$O(s)

Table 3. _____

Calorimeter #	CaCl$_2$·6H$_2$O, g	H$_2$O, g	ΔT, K	q_{soln}, J	ΔH_{rxn}, kJ/mol
1					
2					

Average ΔH_{rxn} = _____ kJ/mol

▶ Attach graph of temperature (°C) vs. time (s) for 2 samples *(title and axes labelled)*
  Label the graph to show how ΔT was determined.

REACTIONS OF HCl AND NaOH

Table 4. _____

Experiment #	Calorimeter #	1.0 M HCl mass, g	1.0 M NaOH mass, g	ΔT, K	q_{soln}, J	ΔH_{rxn}, kJ/mol L.R.*
1	1					
1	2					
2	1					
2	2					

* ΔH_{rxn} _should be reported per mole of limiting reagent (L.R.) in the reaction between HCl and NaOH._

Average ΔH_{rxn} = _____ kJ/mol of L.R.

▶ Attach graphs of temperature (°C) vs. time (s) for experiment #1 and experiment #2 _(title and axes labelled)_

Sample calculation of q_{soln} (J) for experiment # _____ in calorimeter # _____:
(Show all work, label units and check your signs.)

Note assumption(s) used in the calculation of q_{soln}:

Sample calculation of ΔH_{rxn} (kJ/mol) for experiment # _____ in calorimeter #_____:

The limiting reactant (L.R.) in this reaction was _____.
(Show all work and label units.)

Note assumption(s) used in the calculation of ΔH_{rxn}:

DISCUSSION

(Answer the questions on p. 102 of your lab manual. Use reverse and/or add additional paper if necessary.)

CHAPTER 9

HOW CAN ABSORPTION OF LIGHT BE USED TO DETERMINE THE CONCENTRATION OF A COMPOUND IN SOLUTION?

Spectrophotometric methods can be used to determine the concentration of components in solution. Compounds and ions that have color absorb visible light differently at different wavelengths. The amount of light absorbed depends on the identity of the molecules and their concentrations.

▶ **Read Spectroscopy: An Introduction, Appendix C.**

Careful measurement is very important when attempting to find the concentration of solutions. Volumetric techniques must be performed with care.

▶ **Review the Volumetric Measurement Techniques information in Appendix B, especially pipet, buret, and volumetric flask use.**

In this lab, you will determine the Fe^{2+} concentration in solutions using spectrophotometric techniques by converting colorless Fe^{2+} to a red-orange complex by adding 1,10-phenanthroline ("phen").

$$Fe^{2+}(aq) + 3 \ phen(aq) \rightarrow Fe(phen)_3^{2+}(aq)$$

colorless   colorless   red-orange

Measurements in the visible region of the electromagnetic spectrum will be made using the solution containing the colored complex ion, $Fe(phen)_3^{2+}$. Knowing the concentration of $Fe(phen)_3^{2+}$ in a solution, you can calculate the concentration of Fe^{2+} in the original sample.

As you carry out this experiment, you will apply the measurement and analysis procedures of visible spectroscopy, which include:

- determination of an appropriate wavelength to make absorbance measurements
- preparation of standard solutions
- construction of a calibration plot (absorbance vs. concentration)
  - measure absorbance of standard solutions
  - graph the absorbance vs. concentration data for the standard solutions
  - obtain the best-fit straight line through the data points
  - print the graph and equation of the best-fit straight line
  - obtain the molar absorptivity, ε
- determination of the concentrations of Fe^{2+} in two unknown solutions

Procedure

Lab work is done in groups of 3 or 4 students. Each student must record a complete set of data in his/her lab notebook and turn in the duplicate copy of the data on the perforated pages from the lab notebook at the end of the lab period. You may be required to complete a formal lab report outside of lab, so it is very important that the data in your lab notebook is complete (i.e. it should contain everything you will need to write your report.) Your group must also print and save any graphs that must be attached to your report.

WASTE: All solutions used in this experiment can be disposed of down the drain.

Clean and Set Up the Measuring Equipment and Glassware

Our tap water contains iron, which will interfere with your results, so rinse all pieces of glassware thoroughly with deionized water.

Your group will need the following for the analysis:

- a 10-mL graduated cylinder and 100-mL beaker to prepare the blank solution

- a 100–mL beaker and a 25.00-mL buret for 2.50×10^{-4} M $(NH_4)_2Fe(SO_4)_2$, ammonium iron (II) sulfate, your source of Fe^{2+} for the standard solutions

- a 250-mL beaker and a 50.00-mL buret for 0.0055 M 1, 10-phenanthroline

- four 25.00-mL volumetric flasks for preparation of standards

- two 50.00-mL volumetric flasks for preparation of unknown iron solutions

- two 100-mL beakers for unknown Fe^{2+} solutions

- a 10.00-mL pipet for preparation of unknown iron solutions

Dry the beakers. All other pieces of glassware do not need to be dry.

Label all glassware so that you do not confuse the contents of each beaker, buret or flask.

Obtain the following solutions:

    40 mL of 2.50×10^{-4} M $(NH_4)_2Fe(SO_4)_2$

    60 mL of 0.0055 M 1,10-phenanthroline

    25 mL of each unknown Fe^{2+} solution, A and B

You will dispense ammonium iron (II) sulfate and 1,10-phenanthroline from burets.

▶ **Review "Using a buret to measure liquid volumes" in Appendix B."**

Preparation of a Blank Solution and Fe(phen)$_3$$^{2+}$ Standard Solutions

You will prepare a blank or control solution and four standard solutions of Fe(phen)$_3$$^{2+}$.

A blank solution is a solution that contains all components of a potential sample (such as the solvent and solutes) except for the species of interest. For this analysis the blank solution will contain deionized water (the solvent) and phenanthroline (one of the solutes). You will set the spectrophotometer to zero absorbance with this solution. By setting the spectrophotometer to zero absorbance with the blank solution, we adjust the instrument to correct for any light absorbed by deionized water and phenanthroline.

Prepare the blank. Using a 10 mL graduated cylinder, measure 5 mL of deionized water and pour into a clean, dry 100 mL beaker. Dispense 5.00 mL of phenanthroline from the buret into the beaker and mix.

Prepare standards. Label four 25.00 mL volumetric flasks 1 - 4. Use burets to dispense the quantities of 2.50 x 10^{-4} M (NH$_4$)$_2$Fe(SO$_4$)$_2$ and 0.0055 M 1,10-phenanthroline indicated in Table 9.1 into the labeled volumetric flasks. Carefully, add deionized water to the calibration mark on the neck of the volumetric flask. Seal the opening of the flask with Parafilm and invert several times to mix.

Table 9.1. Preparation of Fe(phen)$_3$$^{2+}$ Standard Solutions

Standard #	Volume of 2.50 x 10^{-4} M (NH$_4$)$_2$Fe(SO$_4$)$_2$ (mL)	Volume of 0.0055 M 1, 10-phenanthroline (mL)
1	2.00	5.00
2	4.00	5.00
3	6.00	5.00
4	9.00	5.00

Preparation of the Unknown Solutions for Measurement

▶ **Review "Using a Pipet to Measure Liquid Volumes" Appendix B.**

Pipette 10.00 mL of unknown solution A into a labeled 50.00-mL volumetric flask. Add 5.00 mL of 0.0055 M 1,10-phenanthroline ("phen") **from the buret**. Add deionized water to the middle mark on the flask. Seal the flask with Parafilm and invert several times to mix. Repeat with unknown solution B.

DATA COLLECTION

▶ **Review Appendix C, Spectroscopy: An Introduction**

Connect the SpectroVis Plus spectrophotometer to the computer

- Start the Logger Pro application.
- Connect the SpectroVis spectrophotometer to the computer with the USB cable

Set the Spectrometer to Zero

- Rinse and fill a cuvette about ¾ full with the blank solution (see p. 109).
- From the **Experiment** menu choose **Calibrate Spectrometer:**.
- The calibration dialog box will display the message: "Waiting 90 seconds for lamp to warm up."
- When you see "Warmup complete", place the cuvet with the blank in the sample chamber of the spectrophotometer.
- Click **Finish Calibration**.
- Click **OK**.

Collecting a Spectrum to Determine the Wavelength of Maximum Absorbance

- Click the **Configure Spectrometer** 🏛 button
- Select **Absorbance vs. Wavelength** as the collection mode.
- Rinse and fill a cuvette about ¾ full with standard #3.
- Place the cuvet in the sample chamber of the spectrophotometer.
- Click the `▶ Collect` button.
- Wait 10 seconds.
- Click the `■ Stop` button to end data collection.
- An absorption spectrum of $Fe(phen)_3^{2+}$ should be visible in a Logger Pro window. Click `🔠` to autoscale the graph.
- Store the spectrum data by choosing **Store Latest Run** from the **Experiment** menu.

  (Note: This will move the latest data set to columns at the end of the table, creating a new set of empty columns at the beginning of the table, ready to receive the next set of new data. You may need to scroll through the columns or make the table window wider in order to see the data columns at the end of the table.)

Selection of the Wavelength for Making Absorbance Measurements

From the absorption spectrum of $Fe(phen)_3^{2+}$, find the wavelength at which the absorbance is a maximum (λ_{max}) by clicking ⌧ and placing the mouse at the highest point of the peak. This is the best wavelength for measuring the absorbance of $Fe(phen)_3^{2+}$, which will be used to determine the concentration of $Fe(phen)_3^{2+}$. Record this wavelength in your lab notebook and make all absorption measurements of the standards and samples at this wavelength.

Generate a Calibration Plot using the Standard Solutions

Using the information given in Table 9.1, calculate the molarity of $Fe(phen)_3^{2+}$ in each of the 4 standards solutions after the 1,10-phenanthroline (phen) has been added and then diluted to final volume of 25.00 mL. Note that the phen is in excess in this experiment, so Fe^{2+} is the limiting reagent and all the Fe^{2+} will be converted to $Fe(phen)_3^{2+}$. Create a table in your lab notebook to record each standard's concentration and absorbance.

Absorbance Measurements of the Standard Solutions

- Click the **Configure Spectrometer** 🏛 button

- Select **Absorbance vs. Concentration** as the **Collection Mode**.

- Set the **Column Name** to "Concentration", the **Short Name** to "conc", and the **Units** to "mol/L".

- Select the wavelength to use for absorbance measurements (Note: if the cuvette containing standard #3 is still in the spectrophotometer, the wavelength of maximum absorbance, λ_{max} will be automatically selected), then click **OK**.

- When you are ready to collect absorbance-concentration data for the standards, click the ▶Collect button.

- For each of the 4 standards, in order from the least concentrated (#1) to the most concentrated (#4):

  1. Rinse the cuvette with a small amount of the standard solution by rolling the solution in the cuvette.

  2. Fill the cuvette about ¾ full with the standard solution.

  3. Wipe the outside of the cuvette with a Kimwipe. Insert the cuvette into the spectrophotometer.

  4. Wait a few seconds, press the ⊛Keep button, type the concentration in the edit box (NOTE: 1.00×10^{-3} must be entered as 1.00E-3), and press **Enter.**

  5. Record the absorbance of the standard in your lab notebook.

After you have recorded the absorbance of all the standards, click the ■Stop button. Some of the points may not be on the graph so click ⫼A to autoscale the graph. Save your data. (See instructions on the next page.)

Calibration Plot for Fe(phen)$_3$$^{2+}$

A calibration plot of the absorbance of Fe(phen)$_3$$^{2+}$ at the known concentrations of the standards should be visible in a Logger Pro window. Click on the **Linear Fit** ⬚ button to find the equation of the best-fit straight line and display the equation on the graph. The equation of the line corresponds to the following equation known as the Beer-Lambert law:

absorbance = (molar absorptivity) x (path length) x (concentration)

Since the path length in this experiment is 1.0 cm, the slope of the line is the molar absorptivity.

Print your calibration plot for inclusion with your report. Make sure the title and axes are labeled. (See instructions below.)

Analysis of the Prepared Unknown Solutions

For each prepared unknown solution:

1. Rinse, then fill the cuvette about ¾ full with the prepared unknown solution. Wipe the outside of the cuvette with a Kimwipe. Insert the cuvette into the spectrophotometer.

2. Record the absorbance value displayed in the lower left box into your lab notebook.

Saving Data

Data can be saved into a Logger Pro file (.cmbl) by selecting **Save As…** from the **File** menu. This file type can only be opened properly by the Logger Pro program. You can also save the data as an Excel file, if desired (see below).

Printing

Before printing, change the paper orientation from **Portrait** to **Landscape**.

From the **File** menu, select **Page Setup**, then select the **Landscape** option, then click **OK**

One can print the windows as they appear on the screen (Data Table and Graphs) on a single page by:

1. From the **File** menu, select **Print**
2. If the **Print Options** window appears:
   a. Check the **Print Footer** option
   b. for **Name:**, enter the names of the people in the group
   c. for **Comment:**, enter the title of the lab
   d. Click "**OK**"
3. Click "**OK**"

To print a single graph, enlarge the window containing the graph to fill the screen, then use the **Print** command as above.

The **Print Preview** command will show what the page from the **Print** command will look like when printed.

Data Export to Excel (optional)

To take the data collected by Logger Pro and transfer it to an Excel spreadsheet for further analysis or additional calculations, you can either:

1. Export the data into a .csv format file by selecting **File** menu > **Export As** > **CSV...** .

   or

2. Select the data in the data table in Logger Pro, then select **Copy** from the **Edit** menu. Switch to the Excel program and use the **Paste** option to insert the data into the Excel spreadsheet.

You will have to manually provide titles for the columns, so make sure you can identify these appropriately.

Waste Disposal and Cleanup

Disconnect the spectrophotometer and return it to your instructor.

All solutions can be poured down the drains followed with water. Cuvets are discarded in the trash.

Rinse all glassware at least three times with distilled water. Return the pipet and 25 mL volumetric flasks to your instructor. Return all other glassware to appropriate locations.

Keep your safety goggles on until you have completed the data analysis, obtained any results that are needed from other groups, and are leaving lab.

Lock your lab drawer before leaving lab.

DATA ANALYSIS

Using the absorbance value for your unknown solution and the $Fe(phen)_3^{2+}$ calibration plot, calculate the concentration of $Fe(phen)_3^{2+}$ in the diluted unknown solutions. Then, calculate the concentration of Fe^{2+} in the original Fe^{2+} unknown solutions.

▶ **Be sure to take into account any dilutions that you made!**

Compare the experimental concentration of $Fe(phen)_3^{2+}$ you determined to the actual value provided by your instructor by calculating the % error in your experimental values.

$$\% \text{ error} = \frac{|\text{experimental-theoretical}|}{\text{theoretical}} \times 100$$

RESULTS

Collect and record the following data from **at least three other groups** in your laboratory section:

- wavelength of light used
- molar absorptivity of $Fe(phen)_3^{2+}$ at this wavelength
- original concentrations of Fe^{2+} in the two unknown solutions

Record your group's results as well.

Which values in the results from your group and other groups would you use to calculate a reliable average value of the Fe^{2+} concentrations of the unknown solutions? Explain the criterion you used to decide which values could/could not be used to calculate a reliable average. Then calculate an average value based on your stated criterion.

PREPARATION FOR "WHERE'S THE IRON?"

While you are waiting for results from other groups and/or before you leave lab today, work with your lab group to calculate the concentration of the standard solutions that you will prepare next week (see p. 123). Next, decide who in the group is going to do which parts of the experiment (see p. 120). Before you leave lab today, turn in the duplicate copy of your lab notebook pages containing the concentrations of the standards and the list of duties.

DISCUSSION

1. Suppose a student who took CHM 11500 last semester told you that the molar absorptivity of $Fe(phen)_3^{2+}$ is equal to 1.1×10^4. Describe why you would still need to construct a calibration plot in order to determine the concentration of Fe^{2+} in an unknown solution.

2. In this analysis, you made inferences about the concentration of Fe^{2+} using measurements of $Fe(phen)_3^{2+}$ solutions but never made a stoichiometry conversion between Fe^{2+} and $Fe(phen)_3^{2+}$. What assumption about the reaction between Fe^{2+} and "phen" has been made for this analysis procedure?

LAB NOTES

Each student must turn in laboratory notebook duplicate pages containing a complete data set and observations for the experiment **at the end of the lab period.**

LAB REPORT

You and your partner or group will turn in one completed report, either a formal lab report or a completed lab report form at the end of this chapter. It is your responsibility as a group to ensure that everyone whose name is on the report has participated as fully as possible in the completion of the project.

The report or report form is an organized summary of your work and does not replace the need to keep a complete set of lab or field notes in your lab notebook as the lab is being done and data collected.

Title: _____

Work Done and Report Prepared by: _____

Date: _____ Lab Section Number: _____

GOAL(S)

DATA

Write the equation for the chemical reaction used to convert Fe^{2+} to a colored species:

Preparation of the Blank Solution *(describe how you prepared the blank)*

Selection of Wavelength for Absorbance Measurements

Solution used for wavelength scan: _____

▶ *Attach absorbance vs. λ plot with title and axes labeled.*

λ at which $Fe(phen)_3^{2+}$ has maximum absorbance = _____

Spectrophotometric Analysis of Standard Solutions

Table 1. _____ *(enter appropriate titles for all Tables)*

Standard Solution #	Fe^{2+} Concentration, M	Absorbance

Sample calculation of Fe^{2+} concentration in Standard Solution #_____:
(show work including molar ratio(s) and label units)

Preparation of Unknown Solution Samples
(describe how you prepared samples of the unknowns for spectrophotometric analysis)

Spectrophotometric Analysis of Unknown Solutions

Table 2. _____

Unknown Solution	Absorbance at _____ nm

DATA ANALYSIS

Calibration Plot (Standard Curve)

▶ *Attach Calibration Plot (Standard Curve) with title and axes labeled.*

Calibration Plot (Standard Curve) Information

      equation for line: (at _____ nm): _____

Concentration of Unknown Solutions

Table 3. _____

Unknown Solution	Fe^{2+} Concentration in diluted sample, M	Fe^{2+} Concentration in original solution, M

Sample calculation of Fe^{2+} concentration in unknown solution _____
(show all work including molar ratio(s); label units)

      diluted sample:

      original solution:

RESULTS

Percent Error

Table 4. _____

Unknown Solution	Fe^{2+} Concentration (actual/theoretical), M	Fe^{2+} Concentration (experimental), M	Percent Error
A			
B			

Sample calculation of % error of $[Fe^{2+}]$ in unknown _____:
(show work and label units)

DATA AND RESULTS FROM OTHER GROUPS (AT LEAST 3)

Table 5. _____

Group	λ	Molar Absorptivity	Original $[Fe^{2+}]$

Explanation of criteria for selecting which values would give a reliable average $[Fe^{2+}]$:

Average $[Fe^{2+}]$ = _____

DISCUSSION
(Answer the questions found on p. 114 of your lab manual. Attach additional paper if needed.)

PREPARATION FOR "WHERE'S THE IRON?" LAB: Calculate the concentrations of the standard solutions you will prepare next week and decide who is going to do which parts of the lab. Record your calculation results and decisions in your lab notebook pages. Turn in the duplicate lab notebook pages.

CHAPTER 10

WHERE'S THE IRON?*

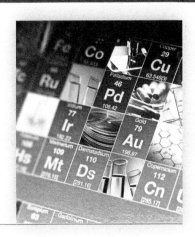

PURPOSE

Iron is an essential element for mammals, plants and some single celled organisms. Iron is important for oxygen transport, electron transfer in the mitochondria and the function of many enzymes in living organisms. Humans get their iron by eating meats, vegetables and beans.

The purpose of this experiment is to determine the amount of iron in just one vegetable, broccoli, and compare your experimental results to values reported by a reliable internet source. You will also determine if the iron is evenly distributed throughout the broccoli by comparing the amount of iron found in broccoli stems to the amount found in florets. If the iron is not distributed equally, which part of the vegetable contains the highest amount of iron? Where is the iron?

You will accomplish this analysis by first dry-ashing a sample of the broccoli. *Dry-ashing is* a method used to decompose organic samples by heating in an open crucible until all carbonaceous matter has oxidized, leaving a residue of inorganic components.

You will add hydrochloric acid, HCl, to the ash to dissolve the iron. The dissolved iron will be in the Fe^{3+} form in this solution. Next, you will add potassium thiocyanate ion (KSCN) to samples of the filtered solution. The iron ion, Fe^{3+}, and potassium thiocyanate will react according to the equation below.

$$Fe^{3+}(aq) + 6\ SCN^-(aq) \rightarrow [Fe(SCN)_6]^{3-}(aq)$$
$$\text{colorless} \qquad \text{colorless} \qquad \text{red-orange}$$

Note that colorless solutions of Fe^{3+} and potassium thiocyanate react to produce a colored species, $[Fe(SCN)_6]^{3-}$.

You know from the previous experiment that the concentration of a colored species is proportional to its absorbance as measured by a spectrophotometer according to Beer-Lambert law. To find the concentration of $[Fe(SCN)_6]^{3-}$ you must first prepare a calibration plot of absorbance versus the concentration of $[Fe(SCN)_6]^{3-}$ using solutions of known $[Fe(SCN)_6]^{3-}$ concentration that you will prepare from a stock solution. The concentration of $[Fe(SCN)_6]^{3-}$ in the broccoli samples will be determined by comparing the absorbance of the samples with information from the $[Fe(SCN)_6]^{3-}$ calibration plot that you construct.

---

* Originally abstracted in part from P. E. Adams, *J. Chem. Educ.* 1995, 72, 649 by J. Nash, Purdue University.

PROCEDURE

Lab work is done in groups of three or four students. Each member of the group must record a complete set of data in his/her lab notebook and turn in the duplicate copy of the data on the perforated pages from the lab notebook at the end of lab. Since you may be required to complete a formal lab report outside of lab, it is very important that the data in your lab notebook is complete (i.e. it should contain everything you will need to write your report.) Print and save the graphs that you will need to complete your report.

! WEAR GLOVES. If you leave the lab, take the gloves off and recycle them so you don't transport any hazardous materials that might be on the gloves outside of the lab. Get new gloves when you return to lab.

What Part of the Vegetable Will You Analyze?

Your instructor will assign your group to analyze either the broccoli stems or florets. Keep in mind that the goal is to determine whether iron is evenly distributed throughout the vegetable and, if not, what part of the vegetable contains the most iron.

Three Procedures to Work on Simultaneously

Your group should accomplish three things before you get to the point where you add thiocyanate solution to any standard or vegetable sample. See p. 123 for details.

1. Prepare the vegetable sample.

2. Clean and set up the measuring equipment.

3. Prepare standard solutions.

Prepare the Vegetable Sample

Weigh about 5 grams (±10%) of broccoli into a weigh cup. Mince the sample into very small pieces if necessary.

Find the mass of a clean, dry evaporating dish to the nearest 0.001 g. Transfer the minced broccoli into the evaporating dish and find the mass of the evaporating dish and broccoli. Record the exact mass of the broccoli sample in your notebook.

Dry-Ashing of the Broccoli

The ashing process will smell and produce smoke, so it must be done in a student bench hood. The student bench hoods can be found in the cabinets under the main hoods. Your instructor will show you how to use it properly. Work as far inside the bench hood as possible. Put the evaporating dish on a wire gauze, supported by a ring on a stand, so that the bottom of the evaporating dish will be several inches above the Bunsen burner. See Figure 10.1 on the next page.

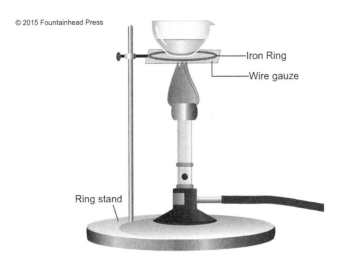

© 2015 Fountainhead Press

Iron Ring

Wire gauze

Ring stand

Figure 10.1. Heating the Broccoli Sample

←barrel

←air vents

gas needle valve

Figure 10.2. Bunsen Burner

It is important that you are familiar with the parts of a Bunsen burner, as shown in Figure 10.2.

The gas needle valve controls the rate at which methane (CH_4) gas enters the burner and determines the size of the flame.

The air vents control the rate at which air enters the burner.

Methane and air mix in the burner barrel and produce a flame whose temperature is determined by the ratio of air (oxygen) to methane (fuel).

Turning on the Bunsen burner

▶ **IF ANY PROBLEM OCCURS, TURN THE GAS OFF AT THE TAP IMMEDIATELY.**

1. Close the needle valve at the base of the burner.

2. Close the air vents by turning the barrel in the clockwise direction.

3. Make sure the tubing is in good condition and securely connected to the inlet at the base of the burner.

4. Connect the other end of the tubing to the gas nozzle at your lab station. At this point, the gas valve at your lab spot should be in the "off" position (valve handle is perpendicular to the nozzle).

5. Remove any flammable or unnecessary items from near the burner.

6. Open the needle valve at the base of the burner a half turn.

7. Light a match.

8. Turn the gas valve at the lab station to the "on" position (valve handle is parallel to the nozzle.).

9. Bring the lit match alongside the barrel of the burner and raise it slowly to the top edge of the barrel. Once the burner is lit, extinguish the match with water and discard it in the trash.

10. At this point the flame is yellow and flickering (safety flame).

11. Turn the barrel of the burner counter-clockwise to open the air vents. As you increase the air vent opening, the flame should become a light blue, almost invisible flame (medium flame).

12. **CAUTION:** Do not turn the barrel so far that it detaches from the burner (>10 turns).

13. One can achieve a hotter flame by continuing to increase the air supply until a blue inner cone appears (hottest flame). The hottest point is at the tip of the inner blue cone.

14. Adjust the needle valve of the burner to achieve the desired flame height and size. **For this experiment, you need a blue flame with an inner cone that is a couple inches high.** (Your instructor can assist you with adjusting the Bunsen burner so that you have an optimum flame.)

    CAUTION: The valve can fall out if turned too far (>10 turns). You may also need to adjust the air vent as you increase or decrease the gas flow to achieve the proper blue flame.

Place the Bunsen burner under the evaporating dish so that the bottom of the evaporating dish is just above the tip of the inner cone (hottest part of the flame).

Heat (or ash) the sample until the broccoli sample is reduced to a grey ash. This will take at least 30 minutes. During this process, you will first observe the sample steaming and/or smoking. Next, you will observe charring, and then glowing embers. Eventually, your sample will consist almost entirely of grey ash. While the broccoli is ashing, work on the tasks in the section "**During Ashing Process.**"

When your broccoli sample is nearly all grey ash with very few black pieces and no moisture remaining (or if the sample has been ashed for at least 60 minutes), the ashing process is complete and you can turn off the Bunsen burner by closing the gas valve on the lab bench.

▶ **Be careful at this point because the ash is very light and can be disturbed by the slightest draft.**

Using tongs, put the evaporating dish on a white heat resistant pad. Cover the evaporating dish with a watch glass to prevent the loss of the ash. Allow the dish to cool to room temperature.

Continue to the section "**After Ashing Process**" to continue the experiment.

During Ashing Process

While your broccoli sample is ashing, work on the tasks below. Note in your report which team member is responsible for each task.

1. Clean and set up the measuring equipment and glassware below. Since our tap water contains iron, which will interfere with your results, rinse everything thoroughly with deionized water. The test tubes must be dried after rinsing. Label the burets and test tubes so you don't confuse the samples or solutions.

    ▪ 1 25.00-mL buret for 0.00020 M Iron(III) chloride, $FeCl_3$

    ▪ 1 25.00-mL buret for 1.0 M Potassium thiocyanate, KSCN

    ▪ 1 50.00-mL buret for 2 M Hydrochloric acid, HCl

    ▪ 8 medium sized test tubes for the standards and sample solutions

2. Prepare the standard solutions.

3. Calculate the concentrations of the standard solutions.

4. When the spectrophotometer is warmed up, analyze your standard solutions and create your calibration plot.

Preparation and Analysis of $[Fe(SCN)_6]^{3-}$ Standard Solutions

You will prepare 5 standard solutions (each with a total volume of 15.00 mL), calculate their concentration, and measure the absorbance of each standard to generate your calibration plot.

Table 10.1. Preparation of Standard Solutions for $[Fe(SCN)_6]^{3-}$ calibration plot.

Standard #	Volume of 0.00020 M $FeCl_3$ (mL)	Volume of 2 M HCl (mL)
Blank	0	10.00
1	0.20	9.80
2	0.40	9.60
3	1.00	9.00
4	2.00	8.00
5	3.00	7.00

Rinse and fill the 3 burets with the solutions that you will use to prepare the standards (0.00020 M $FeCl_3$, 2 M HCl, and 1.0 M KSCN).

Prepare 5 standard solutions by first adding the $FeCl_3$ solution and the HCl to the labeled test tubes as shown in Table 10.1. (You will not add the KSCN solution until you are ready to make the absorbance measurements.)

DATA COLLECTION

Connect the SpectroVis Plus spectrophotometer to the computer

- Start the Logger Pro application.

- Connect the SpectroVis spectrophotometer to the computer with the USB cable

Set the Spectrometer to Zero

- Rinse and fill a cuvette about ¾ full with the blank solution. (see Table 10.1)

- From the **Experiment** menu, choose **Calibrate Spectrometer:**.

- The calibration dialog box will display the message: "Waiting 90 seconds for lamp to warm up."

- When you see "Warmup complete", place the cuvette with the blank in the sample chamber of the spectrophotometer.

- Click **Finish Calibration**.

- Click **OK**.

Collect an Absorption Spectrum to Determine the Wavelength of Maximum Absorbance

- Click on the **Configure Spectrometer** 🏠 button

- Select **Absorbance vs. Wavelength** as the **Collection Mode**, then click **OK**.

- Prepare a solution containing $[Fe(SCN)_6]^{3-}$ by combining 1.00 mL 0.00020 M $FeCl_3$, 9.00 mL 2 M HCl, and 5.00 mL 1.0 M KSCN in a test tube. Use a small square piece of Parafilm to seal the test tube and invert to mix.

- Rinse and fill the cuvette about ¾ full with this solution.

- Place the cuvet in the sample chamber of the spectrophotometer.

- Click the ▶ Collect button.

- Wait 10 seconds.

- Click the ■ Stop button to end data collection.

- An absorption spectrum of $[Fe(SCN)_6]^{3-}$ should be visible in a Logger Pro window.

- Store the spectrum data by choosing **Store Latest Run** from the **Experiment** menu.

   (Note: This will move the latest data set to columns at the end of the table, creating a new set of empty columns at the beginning of the table, ready to receive the next set of new data. You may need to scroll through the columns or make the table window wider in order to see the data columns at the end of the table.)

Select the Wavelength for Absorbance Measurements

From the absorption spectrum of $[Fe(SCN)_6]^{3-}$, find the wavelength at which the absorbance is a maximum (λ_{max}). This will be the best wavelength for measuring the absorbance of $[Fe(SCN)_6]^{3-}$, and which should be used to determine the concentration of $[Fe(SCN)_6]^{3-}$. Record this wavelength in your lab notebook and make all absorption measurements of the standards and samples at this wavelength.

Generate a Calibration Plot using the Standard Solutions

Using the information given in Table 10.1, calculate the molarity of $[Fe(SCN)_6]^{3-}$ in each of the 5 standards solutions after the 5.00 mL of KSCN has been added to the test tube. Note that each standard will have a <u>final volume of 15.00 mL</u> after adding the KSCN. Note that the KSCN is in excess in this experiment, so Fe^{3+} is the limiting reagent and all the Fe^{3+} will be converted to $[Fe(SCN)_6]^{3-}$. Create a table in your lab notebook to record each standard's concentration and absorbance.

▶ **Do not add the KSCN solution to a test tube until you are ready to make the absorbance measurement. Once the KSCN solution is added, the sample is stable for only about 15 minutes.**

Absorbance Measurements of the Standard Solutions

- Click on the **Configure Spectrometer** 📊 button
- Select **Absorbance vs. Concentration** as the **Collection Mode**.
- Set the **Column Name** to "Concentration", the **Short Name** to "conc", and the **Units** to "mol/L".
- Click on the wavelength to use for absorbance measurements (Note: if the cuvette containing the solution used to collect the absorption spectra is still in the spectrophotometer, the wavelength of maximum absorbance, λ_{max} will be automatically selected), then click **OK)**.
- When ready to collect absorbance-concentration data for the standards, click the ▶ Collect button.
- For each of the 5 standards, in order from the least concentrated (#1) to the most concentrated (#5):
    1. Add 5.00 mL of 1.0 M KSCN to the solution in the test tube. Use a small square piece of Parafilm to seal the test tube and invert to mix.
    2. Rinse the cuvette with a small amount of the standard solution.
    3. Fill the cuvette about ¾ full with the standard solution.
    4. Wipe the outside of the cuvette with a Kimwipe, and insert the cuvette into the spectrophotometer.
    5. Wait 10 seconds, click on the ⊛ Keep button, type the concentration of $[Fe(SCN)_6]^{3-}$ in the edit box (NOTE: 1.00×10^{-3} must be entered as 1.00E-3), and press **Enter.**
    6. Record the absorbance of the standard in your lab notebook.

After you have recorded the absorbance of all the standards, click on the ■ Stop button. Some of the points may not be on the graph so click 丨A to autoscale the graph. Save your data. (See instructions below.)

Calibration Plot for $[Fe(SCN)_6]^{3-}$

A calibration plot of the absorbance of $[Fe(SCN)_6]^{3-}$ at the known concentrations of the standards should be visible in a Logger Pro window. Click on the **Linear Fit** button to find the equation of the best-fit straight line and display the equation of the line on the graph. The equation of the line corresponds to the following equation known as the Beer-Lambert law:

absorbance = (molar absorptivity) x (path length) x (concentration)

Since the path length in this experiment is 1.0 cm, the slope of the line is the molar absorptivity.

Print your calibration plot for inclusion with your report. Make sure the title and axes are labeled. (See instructions below.)

Saving Data

Data can be saved into a Logger Pro file (.cmbl) by selecting **Save As...** from the **File** menu. This file type can only be opened properly by the Logger Pro program. You can also save the data as an Excel file, if desired (see below).

Printing

Before printing, change the paper orientation from **Portrait** to **Landscape**.

From the File menu, select **Page Setup**, then select the **Landscape** option, and then click **OK**

One can print the windows as they appear on the screen (Data Table and Graphs) on a single page by:

1. From the **File** menu, select **Print**
2. If the **Print Options** window appears:
   a. Check the **Print Footer** option
   b. **for Name:**, enter the names of the people in the group
   c. for **Comment:**, enter the title of the lab
   d. Click "**OK**"
3. Click "**OK**"

To print a single graph, enlarge the window containing the graph to fill the screen, then use the **Print** command as above.

The **Print Preview** command will show what the page from the **Print** command will look like when printed.

Data Export to Excel (optional)

To take the data collected by Logger Pro and transfer it to an Excel spreadsheet for further analysis or additional calculations, you can either:

1. Export the data into a .csv format file by selecting **File** menu > **Export As** > **CSV…** .

   or

2. Select the data in the data table in Logger Pro, then select **Copy** from the **Edit** menu. Switch to the Excel program and use the **Paste** option to insert the data into the Excel spreadsheet.

You will have to manually provide titles for the columns, so make sure you can identify these appropriately.

AFTER ASHING PROCESS

Dissolving the Iron and Filtering the Solution

Make sure you have a clean 50.00-mL buret and 2 clean, dry medium sized test tubes ready.

Very carefully and slowly, begin adding 2 M HCl dropwise from the 50.00-mL buret to the ash in the evaporating dish by allowing it to run down the side of the evaporating dish into the ash until a total of 20.00 mL of HCl has been added.

Stir the solution gently with a glass stirring rod for at least 5 minutes.

Prepare to filter the solution by gravity filtration. Refer to Figure 10.3 and Appendix F: gravity filtration. Fold a piece of filter paper in half, and then in half again forming it into a cone. Place the cone-shaped filter paper in a glass funnel and moisten it to hold it in place.

Place a clean, dry 100-mL beaker below the funnel to collect the filtrate. Slowly pour the solution into the filter paper cone. Do not rinse the evaporating dish or funnel as that will cause the sample solution to be diluted.

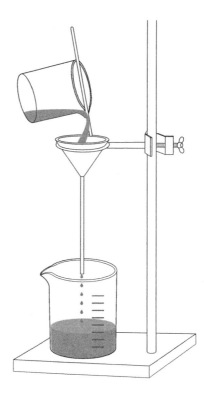

Figure 10.3. Gravity filtration.

Sampling the Filtrate

Prepare two 5.00 mL samples of the filtrate using a 5.00-mL volumetric pipet to transfer 5.00-mL of the filtrate into separate clean, dry medium sized test tubes. Each test tube should contain one 5.00-mL sample.

Preparation and Analysis of Vegetable Samples

Add 5.00 mL of 1.0 M KSCN to vegetable filtrate sample #1. Seal with Parafilm and invert to mix.

Rinse the cuvette with a small amount of sample #1 prepared above by rolling the solution in the cuvette. Discard the rinse into a waste beaker.

Fill the cuvette about ¾ full with sample #1 prepared above. Wipe the outside of the cuvette with a Kimwipe. Insert the cuvette into the spectrophotometer and close the lid.

Measure and record the absorbance of the sample.

Repeat for sample #2.

WASTE DISPOSAL AND CLEANUP

Disconnect the spectrophotometer and return it to your instructor.

All solutions can be poured down the drain followed by a lot of running water. Discard cuvets in the trash.

Rinse all glassware once with tap water followed by a minimum of two rinses with deionized water. Return burets and pipet to your instructor.

Return all reagents to the reagent shelf and equipment to the proper places.

Wipe and dry the tops of the lab benches. Throw paper trash into the trash container.

Keep your splash goggles on until you have completed the data analysis, obtained results from other groups, and are leaving lab.

Lock your lab drawer before leaving lab.

DATA ANALYSIS

Use the absorbance values for each vegetable filtrate sample and the molar absorptivity to calculate concentration of Fe^{3+} in each diluted aliquot.

Use the dilution factor to calculate the concentration (molarity) of Fe^{3+} in the *original* filtrate obtained from treating the ash with HCl.

Use the concentration (molarity) of Fe^{3+} in the original filtrate, the volume of HCl used to dissolve the ash, and the atomic weight of iron to calculate the mass of Fe^{3+} (in milligrams) in the original vegetable sample.

Use the milligrams of Fe^{3+} in the original vegetable sample and the mass of the vegetable sample you started with to calculate the mg Fe^{3+} per gram of vegetable.

Calculate the average mg Fe^{3+} per gram of vegetable.

RESULTS

Write your results (group number, part of vegetable analyzed, λ_{max}, molar absorptivity, and mg Fe^{3+}/g vegetable) on the board to share with the class. Record the results of **at least three other groups** from your lab, at least two of which analyzed a different part of the vegetable than your group.

Calculate the average of the section results for florets and the average of the section results for stems. Calculate the ratio of the average for florets and stems.

Based on your class' results, is there a difference between iron content in the florets versus the stems? If so, which part has more iron? How much more?

Compare your experimental results with the information you obtained from a reliable online source. Comment on the agreement of the results and possible sources of error.

What are some of the possible sources of error in this experiment? Note whether the source of error would cause the results to be falsely low or falsely high.

LAB NOTES

Each student must turn in laboratory notebook duplicate pages containing a complete data set and observations for the experiment **at the end of the lab period.**

LAB REPORT

Your instructor will either provide you with a report form or will provide you with instructions to complete a formal lab report. It is your responsibility as a group to ensure that everyone whose name is on the report has participated as fully as possible in the completion of the project.

CHAPTER 11

HOW DOES MOLECULAR SHAPE AFFECT POLARITY?*

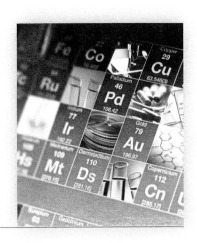

OBJECTIVES

At the end of this activity you should be able to:

- Write Lewis structures for molecules.

- Classify bonds as nonpolar covalent, polar covalent, or ionic based on electronegativity differences.

- Recognize exceptions to the octet rule; draw accurate representations.

- Describe 3-dimensional shapes of simple molecules based on VSEPR theory.

- Predict polarity based on geometry and individual dipole moments.

INTRODUCTION

The substances in our world exhibit remarkably different properties. At room temperature some substances are solids, others liquids, and others gases. Some participate in sudden chemical reactions, whereas others are quite inert and unreactive. Perhaps most remarkably, this wonderful diversity occurs even though the substances are comprised of a limited number of elements. Indeed, only a very small number of different elements are present in almost any pure substance we encounter in the environment or the laboratory. How can this wide diversity of properties be explained?

A key to understanding the wide range of physical and chemical properties of substances is recognizing that atoms *combine* with other atoms to form molecules or compounds and that the *shape or geometry* of a collection of atoms strongly affects the properties of that substance. One reason this occurs is because the distribution of charge in a molecule affects many properties of the substance. For example, if the negative charge is concentrated in one region of a molecule its properties will be widely different than if the charge is distributed evenly throughout the entire molecule.

In this investigation you will examine a theory that chemists use to explain different aspects of chemical bonding: *Valence-shell electron-pair repulsion* (VSEPR) theory. Attention will be given to how molecules are arranged in different shapes and how chemists can predict the geometry of a given molecule. It will then be shown how a molecule's shape, along with electronegativity differences of its atoms, determines the molecule's polarity. As suggested above, the best way to understand and predict the physical and chemical properties of substances in our world is by understanding their structure at the molecular level.

* Prepared by Dr. Ted M. Clark and Dr. Patrick Woodward, the Ohio State University, Department of Chemistry and Biochemistry. Modified by Dr. Christine Hrycyna, and Ms. Marybeth Miller, Purdue University, Department of Chemistry.

The VSEPR model can be used to predict the geometry of molecules and polyatomic ions. *Molecular geometry* describes the positions of the atoms in relation to each other. Included in the description are the *bond angles*, the angles made by the lines joining the bonded atoms. In order to predict geometry using the VSEPR model, we need to know the number of electron pairs in the valence shell of the central atom. That can easily be determined by drawing a Lewis structure.

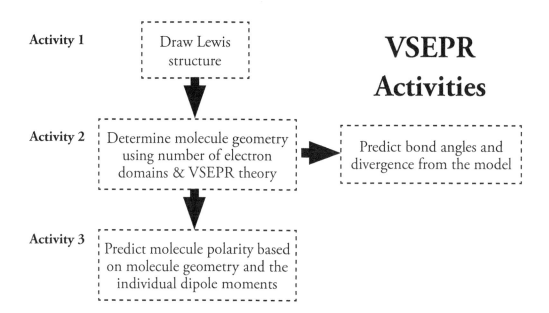

Activity 1 — Draw Lewis structure

VSEPR Activities

Activity 2 — Determine molecule geometry using number of electron domains & VSEPR theory → Predict bond angles and divergence from the model

Activity 3 — Predict molecule polarity based on molecule geometry and the individual dipole moments

In this investigation, you will complete activities that ask you to examine molecular geometry and molecular polarity. These activities are based on computer simulations and ball-and-stick models. **These activities and the report will be completed in lab groups but each group member must participate in the activities and report completion.**

DRAWING LEWIS STRUCTURES

Guidelines for Drawing Lewis Structures

1. Determine the total number of valence electrons; for polyatomic ions remember to adjust for charge.

2. Arrange atoms in a skeleton structure and connect them with single bonds.

   >>> If you are working with a molecule or ion that has three or more atoms, the least electronegative atom is most likely to be the central atom (remembering that hydrogen can only form one bond and therefore is never a likely candidate to be the central atom).

3. Complete octets of the terminal atoms (remember H atoms can only accommodate 2 electrons).

4. If not all of the valence electrons have been used place any extra electrons on the central atom.

   >>> Extra electrons placed on the central atom may in some cases bring the number to more than eight. This is called *expansion of the valence shell* and is an exception to the octet rule; this is acceptable for atoms in the **third period and below**.

5. If the central atom does not have an octet, use lone pairs from terminal atoms to form multiple bonds.

   >>> Only the second period elements C, N, O and sometimes S (in combination with C or O) form multiple bonds. This leads to another exception to the octet rule, i.e. an atom like Be combined with either hydrogen or halogens, as in BeH_2. Since Be does not form multiple bonds, the central atom is electron deficient.

- If more than one acceptable Lewis structure can be drawn by simply choosing a lone pair from a different terminal atom to form a double bond with the central atom, the different structures are called *resonance forms*. The "extra" electron pair is *delocalized*, or spread out among the possible bonding sites.

One reason Lewis structures are useful is because they help to identify the number of *electron domains (groups)*, or regions of high electron density, about a central atom. An electron group can be a bonding pair, a lone pair, or a double or triple bond. A multiple bond is counted as one group.

The Lewis structure for HCN is shown at right. Notice that the central carbon atom has two electron groups (a single bond and a triple bond), which are both bonding electron groups. The nitrogen atom also has two electron groups, but in this case it has one bonding electron group (the triple bond) and one nonbonding electron group (a lone pair of electrons). The hydrogen atom only has one electron group (the single bond).

$$H\!-\!C\!\equiv\!N\!:$$

Once we have a Lewis structure, we have the information needed to predict the geometry. It's important to remember that what we really want to know is the *molecular geometry*—the positions of the atoms in relation to each other. The molecular geometry is dependent on the electron group arrangement; that is why the initial step is drawing the appropriate Lewis structure! As noted above, the simple concept behind valence shell electron pair repulsion theory (VSEPR) is the idea that electron pairs in the valence shell of an atom will repel each other and arrange themselves as far apart as possible. This arrangement of electron pairs determines the geometry of the molecule or polyatomic ion.

ACTIVITY 1: VSEPR AND PREDICTING MOLECULAR GEOMETRY

http://phet.colorado.edu/en/simulation/molecule-shapes

1A. Parent Electron Group Arrangements

Your initial task in this activity is to determine the molecular geometry as the number of electron groups changes. Accomplish this by building structures using **the computer PhET simulation "Molecule Shapes"** and filling in Table 1 on the report form. Start by clicking "Model" and then '**remove all**' and begin with just the central atom. Notice, in this simulation you can increase the number of electron groups by adding single, double, or triple bonds, or lone pair electrons. (For Table 1, use only single bonds for the additional electron domains.) Click on both the molecular geometry box and the electron geometry box in the lower left corner. Click on show bond angles. Molecules can be rotated using the mouse. The first entry in Table 1 has been done for you as an example.

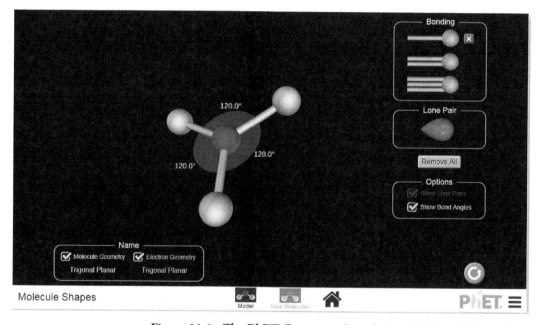

Figure 11.1. The PhET Computer Simulation "Molecule Shapes"

1B. Electron Groups and Molecular Geometries

The molecular geometry is the same as the electron group arrangement if all of the electron groups contain bonding pairs. If lone pair electrons are present on the central atom, the molecular geometry will NOT be the same as the electron group arrangement. To investigate this, return to the simulation and complete Table 2 on the report form by building each of the listed structures using the PhET simulation. Use the model kit to build a three-dimensional model of each of the molecular geometry parent structures (i.e. the structures containing only bonding electron groups and no lone pair electron groups). Show your three-dimensional models to your TA so that s/he can initial your table. Answer questions 1 and 2 on the report form.

1C. Bond Angles

You may have noticed that some electron domains appear larger than others. Refer to the Lewis Structures in your prelab assignment to complete the first column of Table 3 on the report form. Predict the molecular geometry and bond angle for each species. Then, compare your predictions with the experimentally determined bond angles using in the computer simulation under the tab "Real Molecules" at the bottom of the screen. Answer question 3 on the report form.

ACTIVITY 2: MOLECULAR POLARITY

http://phet.colorado.edu/en/simulation/molecule-polarity

Part 2A. Investigating Bond Polarity with the molecule AB

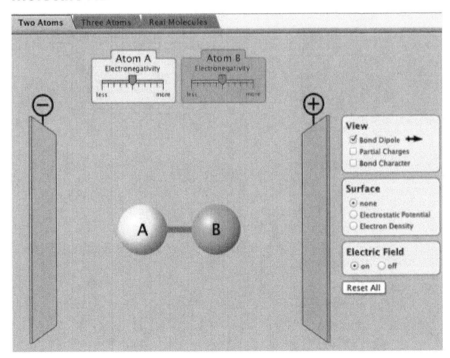

Select the **"Two Atoms"** tab on the top.

In this simulation you will examine the **bond polarity**, which is a measure of how equally the electrons in a bond are shared between the two atoms of the bond.

There are different ways of representing where the electrons are in a bond. Take a few minutes and try the different "views" in the simulation, i.e. bond dipole, partial charges, and bond character. The electron density or electrostatic potential are other ways of communicating where the electrons are in the molecule. Change the relative electronegativities of atoms A and B and observe the result on the bond polarity.

Answer questions 4-6 on the report form.

2B. Molecules in Electric Fields

In this simulation the molecule AB is placed between electric plates (-) and (+) and an electric field can be turned on or off. It is also possible to click on the molecule AB and rotate it to observe the effect in an electric field. Answer questions 7 and 8 on the report form.

2C. Investigating Bond Polarity & Molecular Polarity with the Molecule ABC

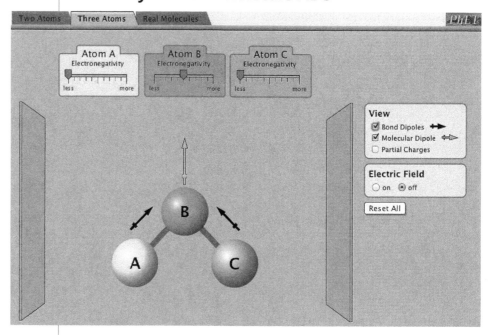

Select the "**Three Atoms**" tab on the top.

In this portion of the simulation you can manipulate molecule ABC. The relative electronegativity of each atom can again be changed. However, it is now also possible to the change the geometry by clicking and dragging an atom to change the angle ∠ABC. Once again, you can spin the entire molecule.

In the view section a new option has been added, **"Molecular Dipole"**. Molecular polarity describes the charge distribution in the entire molecule, not just a bond. If centers of positive and negative charge do not coincide, the molecule is *polar*. How can you predict if a molecule is polar? The two important variables are 1) the bond dipoles in the molecule, and 2) the molecular geometry.

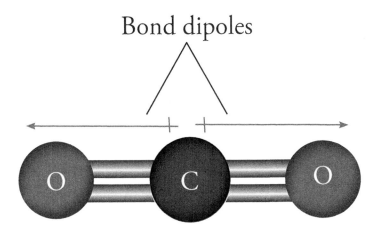

It is important to note that bond dipoles are vector quantities; that is, they have both a magnitude and a direction. In a polyatomic molecule, like ABC, the magnitude and the direction of the individual bond dipoles must be considered when summing vectors. As an example, consider the molecule CO_2. In this molecule there are two bond dipoles because the electronegativity of carbon and oxygen differ. There is no overall molecular dipole, however, because the bond dipoles "cancel" since they are of equal magnitude and are pointed in opposite directions. Carbon dioxide is an example of a *nonpolar molecule* that has polar bonds.

To explore the idea of molecular polarity, complete the first two columns in Table 4 on the report form based on the pictures of the molecules and the bond dipole arrows. Then, construct the molecule in the simulation and see how they behave in the electric field. Were your predictions correct? Rotate the molecules and observe how the vectors add together, subtract or cancel out. (Ignore very, very slight movements of the molecules in the electric field.)

2D. Putting it all together...

Being able to predict the polarity of a molecule is extremely important since many properties of molecules depend on whether they are polar or non-polar. As you have seen in this activity, determining a molecule's polarity is a multi-step process:

Draw Lewis Structure

↓

Use VSEPR to determine molecular geometry

↓

Determine bond polarity (based on electronegativity differences)

↓

Determine molecular polarity based on bond dipoles & molecular geometry

For the species in Table 5 complete this step-by-step process:

- Draw the Lewis Structure (refer to your prelab assignments)
- Identify the molecular geometry
- Predict whether or not there is a molecular dipole
- Check your prediction in the "Real Molecules" section of the simulation

In the simulation you can rotate the molecules. Note how the dipole vectors add together or cancel each other out. Answer question 9 on the report form.

Title: _____

Work Done and Report Prepared by: _____

Date: _____ Lab Section Number: _____

During this lab, partners should take turns operating the computer simulation, filling out the report form, and building three-dimensional models. Evidence of full participation by all group members is several different styles of hand-writing on the report form.

GOAL(S)

ACTIVITY 1: VSEPR AND PREDICTING MOLECULAR GEOMETRY

Part 1A. Parent Electron Group Arrangements

Table 1. Parent Electron Group Arrangements and Bond Angles

Total Number of Electron Groups	Electron Group Arrangement/Geometry	Bond Angles
2	Linear	180°
3		
4		
5		
6		

Part 1B. Electron Groups and Molecular Geometries

Table 2. Summary of Electron Group Arrangements and Molecular Geometry

Total number of electron groups	Electron Bonding Groups	Nonbonding Electron Groups	Electron Group Arrangement/ Geometry	Molecular Geometry	Build a Model (TA initials)
2	2	0			
3	3	0			
3	2	1			
4	4	0			
4	3	1			
4	2	2			
5	5	0			
5	4	1			
5	3	2			
5	2	3			
6	6	0			
6	5	1			
6	4	2			

1. VSEPR stands for "valence-shell electron-pair repulsion". How does electron pair repulsion determine the molecular geometry? Discuss two specific examples from Table 2. (Hint: In the simulation is it possible to force the electron domains to be close together?)

2. **Identify the molecular geometry for each shape.**

   i.

   ii.

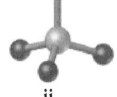

   i   **ii**   **iii**

   iii.

   Determine the electron group arrangement/geometry on which the molecular geometry is based.

   i.

   ii.

   iii.

   How many lone-pairs are on each central atom?

   i.

   ii.

   iii.

Part 1C. Bond Angles

Table 3. Comparison of predicted to experimentally determined bond angles

Molecule	Lewis Structure*	Predicted Molecular Geometry	Predicted Bond Angles	Simulation Result: Experimentally determined bond angles
NH_3				
H_2O				
SO_2				

refer to your work in the prelab assignment

3. Which assumption about the space occupied by nonbonding (lone pair) electron pairs is most consistent with the experimental bond angles: do nonbonding pairs occupy more, less, or the same amount of space as bonding pairs?

ACTIVITY 2: MOLECULAR POLARITY

Part 2A. Investigating Bond Polarity with Molecule AB

4. Explain how the direction of the arrow in the bond dipole symbol (⊢→) relates to the electron density and the partial charges.

5. How does changing the electronegativity of the atoms affect the bond polarity?

6. How does changing the electronegativity of the atoms affect the bond character?

Part 2B. Molecules in Electric Fields

7. What happens to the molecule AB when it has a bond dipole and the electric field is turned on? Spin the molecule around several times and make observations. What happens if the bond dipole is zero?

8. Is there a relationship between the magnitude of the bond dipole and how the molecule is affected by the electric field? If so, explain the relationship.

Part 2C. Investigating Bond Polarity and Molecular Polarity with the Molecule ABC

Table 4. Molecular Polarity

Molecule	Most electronegative atom	PREDICTION: polar or non-polar?	Simulation Result: polar or non-polar?

Part 2D. Putting it all together

Table 5. Molecular Dipoles

Molecule	Lewis Structure*	Molecular Geometry	Prediction: Is there a molecular dipole?	Simulation Result: Polar or non-polar?
N_2				
H_2O				
BF_3				
HCN				
CH_2F_2				
NH_3				
CH_2O				
CO_2				

refer to your work in the prelab assignment

9.

a. What is the difference between Molecular Geometry and Electron Group Arrangement/Geometry?

b. List five characteristics of a molecule that can be determined from a Lewis Structure.

CHAPTER 12

DO YOU SEE THE LIGHT?

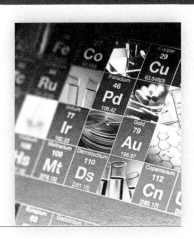

GOALS

The goal of this lab is to synthesize an organic compound and observe its chemiluminescence.

INTRODUCTION

Organic Synthesis

In this experiment, you will synthesize an organic compound known as luminol. Organic compounds are those containing carbon atoms bonded to other carbon or hydrogen atoms and sometimes bonded to other elements.

Organic synthesis is a process whereby organic molecules are treated with reagents or react with other organic molecules to form products that are different from the starting materials. Another definition of organic synthesis from Dr. Steven A. Hardinger of UCLA is "conversion of existing molecules into other useful molecules."

Using organic synthesis, small molecules can be transformed to larger molecules or products not found in nature can be prepared. In addition, existing natural products can be produced or modified.

Organic syntheses can consist of multiple steps to transform the starting materials to the final desired product. Each step will typically transform a portion of the original molecule so that it becomes closer to the desired molecule. The intermediate product may be isolated at each step, removing unreacted reagents or undesired side products, before adding the reagents for the next step.

Synthesis of Luminol

The preparation of luminol is a 2-step synthesis, starting with commercially available 3-nitrophthalic acid and hydrazine. One solid intermediate and the final product luminol (5-amino-1,4-phthalazinedione) are isolated.

3-nitrophthalic acid → (H_2NNH_2) → **5-nitro-1,4-phthalazinedione** → ($Na_2S_2O_4$) → **5-amino-1,4-phthalazinedione (luminol)**

Chemiluminescence of Luminol

After you synthesize luminol, you will react it with 3% hydrogen peroxide, H_2O_2, an oxidizer and potassium ferricyanide, $K_3Fe(CN)_6$, catalyst, in basic solution to produce chemiluminescence. Chemiluminescence is the emission of light as the result of a chemical reaction.

Procedure

Work in groups of 4. Read through the procedures and make sure that each group member is assigned specific tasks.

! **WEAR GLOVES DURING THE ENTIRE PROCEDURE! Before you leave the lab, take the gloves off and recycle them. DO NOT WEAR GLOVES OUTSIDE OF THE LAB. Get new gloves when you return to the lab.**

▶ **USE THE STUDENT BENCH HOODS!**

As you perform the experiment, you should record the operations performed (e.g., added 1.5 spatulas of 3-nitrophthalic acid to ignition tube) or any observations (e.g., yellow solution, temp = 100 °C) into your lab notebook.

Review Appendix E, Using a Bunsen Burner. Before lighting the Bunsen burner, examine the tubing connecting it to the gas nozzle and make sure it is not cracked or broken. When heating with the Bunsen burner, a medium temperature flame that is light blue with no inner cone will be hot enough to heat the solutions, will allow better temperature control than a hotter flame, and make it less likely to break the thermometer. Your TA can assist you with lighting the Bunsen burner and adjusting the flame to the appropriate level.

CAUTION: The thermometer is easily broken and is expensive.

1. Do not stir with the thermometer.
2. Do not allow the thermometer to rest against the ignition tube while heating with the Bunsen burner.
3. Do not place a hot thermometer on the cold bench top.

Part I. Preparing the Luminol

Step 1

Replace two OH groups with NH-NH group

3-nitrophthalic acid

5-nitro-1,4-phthalazinedione

- All of Part I must be performed within a student bench hood.

- Prepare a warm water bath. Add about 150 mL of deionized water to a 250-mL beaker and heat on a hot plate. A setting of "3" should be sufficient.

- Put 15 mL of deionized water into a medium sized test tube, and heat the test tube in the warm water bath.

- Combine approximately 1.5 spatulafuls of 3-nitrophthalic acid and 40 drops of 8% aqueous hydrazine in an ignition tube (not in the largest test tube). Add **two** boiling chips. Clamp this tube vertically on a ring stand. Make sure the opening of the tube is not pointed toward you or any of your lab partners. Heat the mixture by fanning a Bunsen burner under the tube until the solid dissolves. See Figure 12.1 on the next page. Once the solid dissolves, remove the flame.

- Add 3 mL of triethylene glycol to the tube and stir. Place a 260°C thermometer in the mixture. Secure the thermometer with a clamp to a ring stand so that the thermometer bulb is in the mixture, but not touching the tube.

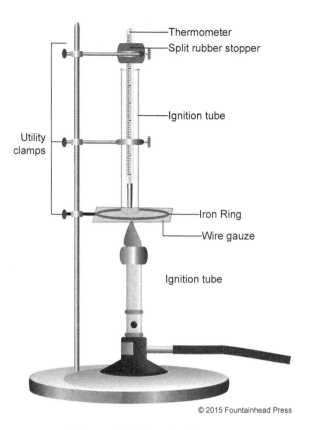

Thermometer
Split rubber stopper

Ignition tube

Utility clamps

Iron Ring
Wire gauze

Ignition tube

© 2015 Fountainhead Press

Figure 12.1. Luminol setup.

! DO THIS STEP VERY CAREFULLY.

- Resume heating the tube with the Bunsen burner, and let the temperature of the mixture rise to about 200 °C, then reduce the heating with the Bunsen burner. (After the flame is removed, the temperature will likely continue to increase. The desired temperature range is 215-220 °C.) For the next 2 minutes, keep the temperature within the range 215–220 °C by fanning the Bunsen burner under the tube. By controlling the amount of time the tube is in the Bunsen burner flame, you should be able to control the temperature.

- Then remove the flame and allow the mixture to cool to about 100 °C.

- Carefully add the previously heated 15 mL of water to this tube.

- Clean and dry the thermometer and return it to your instructor.

- Cool the product by letting cold tap water run down the **outside** of the tube. Hold the test tube with a clamp or **wetted** paper towels. Continue to cool the tube until light yellow solid forms.

- Filter this solid from the mixture using a Büchner funnel and filter paper set up within a student bench hood. Make sure to clamp the filter flask so it doesn't tip over (Büchner funnels are expensive). Rinse the tube out once with deionized water and filter the rinse water in the Büchner funnel.

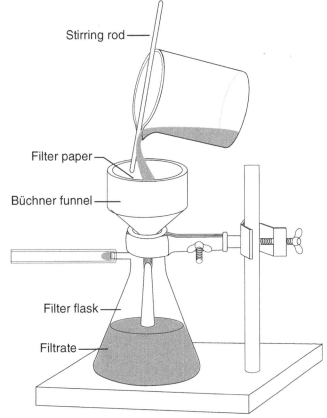

Stirring rod

Filter paper

Büchner funnel

Filter flask

Filtrate

Figure 12.2. Separation technique: suction filtration.

- Gently lift the filter paper out of the Büchner funnel and scrape the solid from the filter paper **using a spatula** and put it back into the ignition tube. (It is not necessary to clean the tube before adding the filtered solid back into it.)

DISCARD THE FILTER PAPER INTO THE WASTE BUCKET.

Step 2

Convert NO$_2$ group to NH$_2$ group

5-nitro-1,4-phthalazinedione   5-amino-1,4-phthalazinedione
                                              luminol

- All of Part II must be performed with a student bench hood.

- Add 5 mL of 10% NaOH to the solid collected in step 1 and stir. A deep brown-red solution results.

- Add 5 spatulafuls of sodium hydrosulfite. Wash the solid down from the walls of the tube with a little deionized water. Add two (2) boiling chips and put a stirring rod into the tube. Clamp the tube onto a ring stand. Make sure the opening of the tube is not pointed toward you or your lab partners.

! DO THIS STEP VERY CAREFULLY.

- Fan the Bunsen burner under the tube and heat the mixture slowly until the mixture boils. **BE VERY CAREFUL OR THE LIQUID WILL SHOOT OUT OF THE TUBE.** Stir with the glass stirring rod and keep the mixture hot for 5 minutes by fanning the Bunsen burner under the tube. The addition of 1–2 boiling chips will help prevent vigorous bumping.

- Carefully add 2 mL of concentrated acetic acid. Cool the tube with cold running tap water as in step 1. Stir the mixture during this cooling process. A precipitate, luminol, should form.

- Collect the luminol by filtration, using a Büchner funnel and filter paper. The filtration must be performed within a student bench hood.

- Remove the boiling chips from the filter paper using forceps. Rinse the chips and put into trash can.

Part II. Chemiluminescence

luminol

- Transfer the filter paper with luminol into a 250-mL beaker. Add 10 mL of 10% NaOH and 90 mL of deionized water. This is Stock Solution A. (The filter paper can stay in the reaction mixture because it will not affect the luminescence or it can be removed with forceps.)

- Next, prepare Solution B in a clean 250-mL Erlenmeyer flask by mixing 20 mL of 3% H_2O_2 and 160 mL of deionized water.

- Place approximately 1 spatulaful of potassium ferricyanide in a 500-mL Erlenmeyer flask.

Demonstrate the following step to your graduate instructor.

- In a dark area, simultaneously add Solution A and Solution B to the 500-mL Erlenmeyer flask. Swirl the flask to increase the brilliance of the luminescence. Time how long the luminescence persists.

WASTE DISPOSAL AND CLEANUP

All filtrates and solutions containing luminol must be placed in the "Liquids" waste container. This includes the first rinse (about 5 mL) of any containers used for the preparation and the luminescence reaction.

Filter paper from both filtration steps is to be discarded in the "Filter Paper" bucket. Paper towels heavily contaminated with chemicals can be placed in this bucket.

Excess solid reagents are to be placed in the "Solids" waste container. Clean up any spilled solids and deposit them into this waste container.

Excess hydrogen peroxide and sodium hydroxide solutions can be rinsed down the sink.

Uncontaminated paper and rinsed boiling chips are to be discarded into the regular trash can.

LAB RECORDS AND REPORTS

Group Portion

You and your partner or group will turn in one completed report, either a formal lab report or a completed lab report form at the end of this chapter. It is your responsibility as a group to ensure that everyone whose name is on the report has participated as fully as possible in the completion of the project.

The report or report form is an organized summary of your work and does not replace the need to keep a complete set of lab or field notes in your lab notebook as the lab is being done and data collected.

Individual Portion

Each student must attach laboratory notebook duplicate pages containing a complete data set and observations for the experiment.

Title: _____

Work Done and Report Prepared by: _____

Date: _____ Lab Section Number: _____

GOAL

Procedure

To summarize the preparation procedure: Complete the table by indicating what materials you used in each process and indicate how the materials were "treated" at each step. Include chemical names and/or structures, amounts, temperatures and procedure steps.

Part I. Preparation of Luminol

	Chemicals (names or formulas or structures) and Amounts	Procedure Notes (What did you do?)
Step 1		
Step 2		

The name of the product recovered at the end of step 1 was:_____.

The material recovered on the filter paper at the end of step 2 was:_____.

Part II. Chemiluminescence

	Chemicals (names or formulas or structures) and Amounts	Procedure Notes (What did you do?)
Solution A Preparation		
Solution B Preparation		
Formula of substance put into the Erlenmeyer flask (the reaction vessel)		

Results

Describe your observations when Solution A, Solution B, and potassium ferricyanide were mixed.

How long did the chemiluminescence persist?

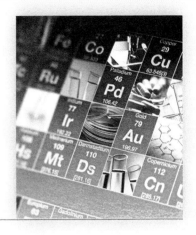

CHAPTER 13

WHAT IS A POLYMER?

INTRODUCTION

During this activity you will prepare and investigate two polymers:

1. cross-linked poly(vinyl alcohol)

2. nylon prepared by the condensation of adipoyl chloride and 1,6-diaminohexane

Read the information on polymers in your textbook and in your lecture notes. It is important that you understand the following terms and skills:

Terms:
- monomer
- polymer
- degree of polymerization
- viscosity
- branched polymers
- cross-linked polymers

Skills:
- calculate the molar mass of a polymer chain, the molar mass of a polymer repeat unit, or the number of repeat units
- identify the repeat unit of a polymer chain
- understand the difference between a condensation reaction and an addition reaction

Cross-linked Poly(Vinyl Alcohol)

Abstracted in part from *J. Chem. Educ.*, 1986, 63 (1), p 57.

Poly(vinyl alcohol) (PVA) is the polymer formed by the ***addition polymerization*** of vinyl alcohol, $H_2C=CHOH$.

vinyl alcohol → addition polymerization → poly(vinyl alcohol)—PVA

Most vinyl polymers are not soluble in water. Poly(vinyl alcohol) is soluble, however, because it has hydroxy (–OH) groups, which can form hydrogen bonds with water, improving its solubility.

Borax (sodium tetraborate, $Na_2B_4O_7 \cdot 10\ H_2O$) dissolves in water to form a mixture of boric acid, $B(OH)_3$, and borate ion, $B(OH)_4^-$. The borate ion can form bonds with the –OH groups in the PVA molecules, connecting together two PVA molecules. These crosslinks are weak enough to be broken under stress.

In this lab you will have the opportunity to observe how this type of crosslinking changes the properties of a polymer.

Nylon

The nylon you will prepare in this experiment is formed by the ***condensation polymerization*** of 1,6-diaminohexane, $H_2N(CH_2)_6NH_2$, an amine, and adipoyl chloride, $ClOC(CH_2)_4COCl$, an acid chloride. The polymerization proceeds with generation of 1 molecule of HCl for each bond formed.

PROCEDURE

! **THESE PROCEDURES INVOLVE HAZARDOUS MATERIALS SO YOU WILL NEED TO WEAR GLOVES FOR ALL YOUR WORK**. If you leave lab, take off the gloves you are wearing and recycle them. Get a new pair of gloves when you return to lab.

Throughout this activity, record your observations paying particular attention to the properties of the reactant(s) and product(s).

Part I. Cross-linking Poly(Vinyl Alcohol)

Work in groups of 3 or 4 students. Follow the instructions and be patient when dissolving the poly(vinyl alcohol).

Preparing the Poly(Vinyl Alcohol) Solution

- Measure 50 mL of deionized water into a 100-mL beaker. Obtain a magnetic stir bar from your instructor and place it in the beaker. Begin heating and stirring the water on a stirrer/hot plate set to "4" for heat and a stir rate of "6".

- Obtain a thermometer from your instructor and carefully insert it into a split rubber stopper. Clamp the thermometer/stopper above the beaker with a utility clamp so that temperature of the water in the beaker can be measured. Make sure the magnetic stir bar doesn't hit the thermometer.

- Heat the water to a temperature between 70° and 80°C.

- Put 3 heaping spatulafuls of solid poly(vinyl alcohol) in a paper weighing cup. (Use the round side of the spatula, not the flat side.)

- Over a period of several minutes, continuously sprinkle the poly(vinylalcohol) onto the surface of the hot water while stirring at a high rotation rate. The granules of polymer must be wetted before the polymer will dissolve.

- Stir until dissolved, keeping the temperature between 70° and 80°C. It is critical to stay within this range because above 80°C, the materials may *permanently* adhere to the beaker. The dissolution may take as long as one hour, so patience is required.

- Once dissolved, allow the PVA solution to cool for 10 minutes before proceeding.

- Transfer the poly(vinyl alcohol) solution into a styrofoam cup. Remove the stir bar.

- *Immediately* clean the beaker and magnetic stir bar with hot water and a brush.

Cross-linking

- Measure 5 mL of borax solution with a graduated cylinder and add it to the PVA solution.

- Use a thick wooden splint to vigorously stir the mixture in the cup for about a minute. Continue stirring until the cross-linked polymer begins to adhere to the splint. Pour any excess liquid down the drain.

- Finish by taking the polymer and kneading it in your hand. Wetting your hands slightly will make handling the polymer less sticky. (Gloves are not required for handling the cross-linked polymer.)

Investigation

Perform the following manipulations with your cross-linked PVA polymer. Comment on the polymer's properties (strength, flexibility, viscosity, etc.). *Each* group member should record his/her observations in his/her lab notebook.

- Suspend the polymer from your hand.

- Pull the polymer slowly.

- Pull the polymer quickly.

- Roll the polymer into a ball and drop it on the lab bench.

- Break off a pea-sized piece of polymer and leave it at rest in a watch glass for a few minutes.

- Break off a pea-sized piece of polymer and place it in a medium sized test tube. Add 1 drop of 1 M HCl. Stir for a minute and record your observations. Next add 2 drops of 1 M NaOH to the test tube. Stir for a minute and record your observations.

- Break off a pea-sized piece of polymer and place it in a medium sized test tube. Add 1 drop of 1 M NaOH to the test tube. Stir for a minute and record your observations.

WASTE DISPOSAL AND CLEANUP

Put the cross-linked PVA inside the styrofoam cup and throw it and wooden splint into the trash can. Wash your hands thoroughly with soap and water.

Return all equipment to its proper location.

Continue to the procedure for the preparation of nylon on p. 161.

RESULTS

Summarize your observations from the polymer manipulations on your lab report worksheet in complete sentences.

DISCUSSION

Answer the following questions on your lab report worksheet:

1. How do the physical properties of poly(vinyl alcohol) (PVA) change as a result of the addition of sodium borate?

    How do you think the physical properties (strength, flexibility, and viscosity) of the polymer would change if *more* borate had been added? Why do you think that?

    How do you think the physical properties (strength, flexibility, and viscosity) of the polymer would change if *less* borate had been added? Why do you think that?

2. Draw a diagram to illustrate how cross-linking poly(vinyl alcohol) changes the physical properties of the polymer. Show the chemical structures of the polymer and the cross-link.

3. How did the addition of acid and base impact the polymer?

At the chemical structure level, what could have led to these observations?

Include chemical structures to help you make your point.

Note: The following reactions occur between the borate ion/boric acid and acid/base:

$$B(OH)_4^- + H^+ \rightarrow B(OH)_3 + H_2O$$

$$B(OH)_3 + OH^- \rightarrow B(OH)_4^-$$

Part II. Preparation of Nylon

This part is to be done in groups of 3 or 4, however, each student will need 100 mL of deionized water in a 600-mL beaker to rinse the nylon thread.

! **Adipoyl chloride is toxic and undiluted adipoyl chloride reacts violently with water. Wear gloves and be sure your equipment is dry.** *ALL* **PARTS OF THIS REACTION MUST BE PERFORMED IN THE MAIN (BIG) HOODS!**

- Combine 10 mL of 1 M 1,6-diaminohexane and 10 mL of 1 M NaOH in a clean 100-mL beaker.

- In a dry 250-mL beaker, combine 20 drops of adipoyl chloride and 20 mL of hexane (measured in a dry 50-mL graduated cylinder). Stir until the mixture is homogeneous.

- From the main hood where the reagents were located, carefully move your beakers to main hood 4 or another available main hood.

- *Slowly and gently,* pour the adipoyl chloride solution from the 250-mL beaker down the side of the 100-mL beaker containing the 1,6-diaminohexane so that two layers form. When properly done, a thin film of nylon will form at the interface between the two immiscible liquids.

If you add the solutions too quickly or in the wrong order, the liquids will mix and a blob of nylon will form and you will not be able to extract nylon "threads."

- One after another, *each student* in the group should take their forceps, reach into the beaker, grab hold of the nylon film, and slowly pull a 30 cm (12 inch) thread. Cut the nylon thread with scissors.

- Immediately place the thread in 100 mL of water contained in a 600-mL beaker. Swirl it around for a few minutes to rinse off excess reagents. Pour the water in the sink while keeping the nylon in the beaker. Add fresh water and wash again.

- Show this product to your instructor. Record your observations in your lab notebook.

WASTE DISPOSAL AND CLEANUP

- Dispose of the nylon in the designated waste jar in the main hood.

- Dispose of the nylon rinse water in the hood sink.

- After each group member obtains their nylon, swirl the contents of the beaker until the reaction is complete. This is the easiest way to dispose of the chemicals—make nylon! Pour the remaining contents of the beaker into the nylon waste container in the main hood.

- Excess hexane and small first rinses of the glassware used to measure nylon reagents should also be disposed of in the nylon waste container.

DISCUSSION

Answer the following questions on your lab report worksheet.

1. In the process of nylon preparation, NaOH was added to the reaction mixture even though it does not appear in the equation for the preparation of nylon. What function does the NaOH have in the process? (Hint: Consider all the products of the nylon reaction.)

2. How many 1,6-diaminohexane monomers and adipoyl chloride monomers are required to make a nylon polymer with a formula weight of 15,000 amu? (As shown in the introduction, one repeat unit consists of the condensation product of one adipoyl chloride molecule and one diaminohexane molecule.)

LAB RECORDS AND REPORTS

Group Portion

You and your partner or group will turn in one completed report, either a formal lab report or a completed lab report form at the end of this chapter.

It is your responsibility as a group to ensure that everyone whose name is on the report has participated as fully as possible in the completion of the project.

The report or report form is an organized summary of your work and does not replace the need to keep a complete set of lab or field notes in your lab notebook as the lab is being done and data collected.

Individual Portion

Each student must attach laboratory notebook duplicate pages containing a complete data set and observations for the experiment.

Title: _____

Work Done and Report Prepared by: _____

Date: _____ Lab Section Number: _____

GOAL *(for the entire lab)*:

PART I: CROSS-LINKING POLY(VINYL ALCOHOL)

Data

A. List and describe the reactants used in Part I.

Chemical Name	Amount	Physical Description

B. Observations from the cross-linking reaction and description of the product:

Results

Summarize your observations from the polymer manipulations.

- Suspend polymer:

- Pull slowly:

- Pull quickly:

- Drop on bench:

- At rest:

- Add HCl:

     Then add NaOH:

- Add NaOH:

Answer the discussion questions on the next page.

Discussion

Answer questions 1-3 for Part I in the space below. Attach extra paper if needed.

PART II: PREPARATION OF NYLON

Data

A. List and describe the reactants used in Part II.

Chemical Name	Amount	Physical Description

B. Observations from the nylon reaction and description of the product:

Answer the discussion questions on the next page.

Discussion

Answer questions 1-2 for Part II in the space below. Attach extra paper if needed.

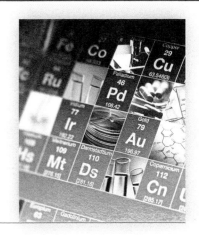

CHAPTER 14

HOW CAN WE ISOLATE BIOLOGICALLY IMPORTANT MOLECULES?

INTRODUCTION

Lipids

Lipids are a group of biomolecules that are classified by a physical property instead of their chemical structure or a particular functional group. Lipids are all biomolecules that are *insoluble* in water due to the high proportion of nonpolar C–H bonds they contain.

The main groups of lipid biomolecules are triglycerols (fats and oils), phospholipids (cell membrane bilayer), prostaglandins (chemical messengers), steroids (hormones), and terpenes (pigments and some vitamins).

In this experiment, you will extract the fat from potato chips. The lipids extracted are all triglycerols, more commonly known as triglycerides. A triglyceride is formed in a dehydration reaction of glycerol with three fatty acids, as shown in Figure 14.1.

$$CH_2-OH \ + \ HO-\overset{\overset{\displaystyle O}{\|}}{C}-R^1 \qquad CH_2-O-\overset{\overset{\displaystyle O}{\|}}{C}-R^1$$

$$CH-OH \ + \ HO-\overset{\overset{\displaystyle O}{\|}}{C}-R^2 \quad \xrightarrow{-3H_2O} \quad CH-O-\overset{\overset{\displaystyle O}{\|}}{C}-R^2$$

$$CH_2-OH \ + \ HO-\overset{\overset{\displaystyle O}{\|}}{C}-R^3 \qquad CH_2-O-\overset{\overset{\displaystyle O}{\|}}{C}-R^3$$

Glycerol   Fatty acids   Triglyceride

Figure 14.1. Formation of triglyceride from glycerol and three fatty acids.

Fatty acids are long chain hydrocarbons with a carboxyl group at its end. The R^n represents various fatty acids. Fatty acids have an even number of carbons in the chain. The most common fatty acids contain between 12 and 20 carbons. Fatty acids without double bonds are called **saturated** fatty acids. Fatty acids with double bonds are known as **unsaturated** fatty acids. Figure 14.2 shows examples of saturated and unsaturated fatty acids. Note that the double bond of unsaturated fatty acids can be in one of two configurations, cis or trans. Most naturally occurring unsaturated fatty acids are of the *cis* configuration.

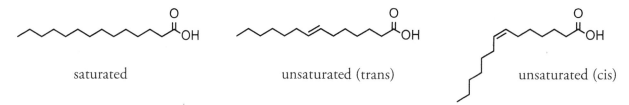

saturated   unsaturated (trans)   unsaturated (cis)

Figure 14.2. Saturated and unsaturated fatty acids.

In this experiment, you will also encounter the chemistry of another class of lipids: the phospholipids. The phospholipids make up the cell membranes in the form of a lipid bilayer, as shown in Figure 14.3 below and in Figure 13.9 in your textbook. Phospholipids compose the cell membrane and consist of a polar phosphate/diglyceride head and two nonpolar fatty acid tails.

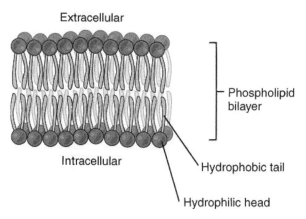

Figure 14.3. Lipid bilayer.

Analysis of Fat Content in Potato Chips

Many nutritional sources recommend that no more than 30% of the Calories in our diet come from fat. However, the *percent* of Calories from fat does not necessarily correspond to the *amount* (mass percent) of fat in food. Different components of food have different energy values, as shown in Table 14.1.

Table 14.1. Energy produced by different components of food.

Component	Energy
Protein or carbohydrate	4 Cal/g
Fat	9 Cal/g

Note the following definitions:

    1 Calorie (as it appears on a nutrition label) = 1000 calories = 1 kcal

    1 calorie = the energy required to raise 1 g by 1 degree Celsius

    1 Calorie = the energy required to raise 1 kg by 1 degree Celsius

As an example, data from the nutrition label of a Big Mac® sandwich is shown in Table 14.2. Fat comprises 13% of the mass of a Big Mac®, but contributes 40% of the Calories.

Table 14.2. Big Mac® nutrition information.

	Weight (g)	% By Weight	Calories	% By Calories
Total	211 g		530 Cal	
Fat	27 g	13%	27 g × 9 Cal/g = 243 Cal	40%
Carbohydrates	47 g	22%	47 g × 4 Cal/g = 188 Cal	35%
Protein	24 g	11%	24 g × 4 Cal/g = 96 Cal	18%

In this experiment you will determine the percent of fat, by weight, in two different kinds of potato chips: original and baked. Potatoes contain a very small amount of fat—just 0.1%—but they will absorb some of the cooking oil when fried or baked.

This procedure involves mixing the chips with a relatively nonpolar solvent that will dissolve the fat and not dissolve the water soluble components of the food such as proteins and carbohydrates. You will then pour the solvent off of the chips, collecting the fat and solvent together. This is known as a solvent extraction. The solvent is then evaporated from the fat and the weight of the fat is measured.

Our procedure is rather simplistic. The analysis used to determine the fat content of food for nutrition labels is more complex than a simple solvent extraction.

You will compare your results to the label information by calculating the percent recovery in your experiment using the following equation:

$$\text{Percent Recovery} = \frac{\text{mass of fat recovered}}{\text{starting or theoretical mass of fat}} \times 100$$

Percent recovery allows you to calculate how much of a compound or solution was lost through a process. Like percent error, this is a useful calculation to determine the effectiveness of a process or technique.

NUCLEIC ACIDS

Nucleic acids contain the chemical information that guides the design, construction and function of all proteins. There are two types of nucleic acids: deoxyribonucleic acid (DNA) and ribonucleic acid (RNA). DNA and RNA are made up of polymers of nucleotides. Each nucleotide unit is made up of a nitrogenous base, a 5-carbon sugar (pentose) and a phosphate group (Figure 14.4). The function of nucleic acid molecules is to encode, transmit, and express genetic material.

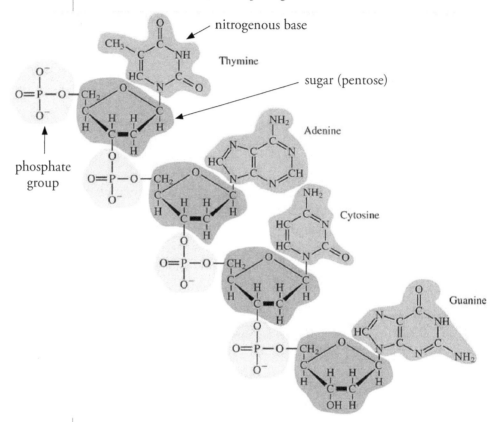

Figure 14.4. Components of DNA.

DNA molecules do not exist as a single polymer of nucleotides, but as two paired polymers that fold around each other to form a double helix. The two polymers run in opposite directions. The phosphate groups form the outer backbone of the helix with the nitrogenous bases in the center of the helix. The helix is stabilized by hydrogen-bonding and the hydrophobic nature of the bases (Figure 14.5).

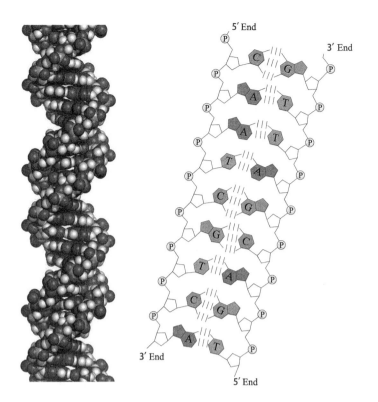

Figure 14.5. DNA double helix structure.

DNA molecules are very large. The human genome contains over a million bases. If the DNA strands were laid out end to end, their length would be as much as 3 meters. The X shaped structure of the chromosome that we often see representing the human genome is achieved by supercoiling of the DNA molecule. In this structure, the DNA is coiled around clusters of proteins known as histone proteins. This DNA-protein complex is known as a nucleosome and is further condensed to form a supercoiled fiber of DNA that forms a chromosome (Figure 14.6).

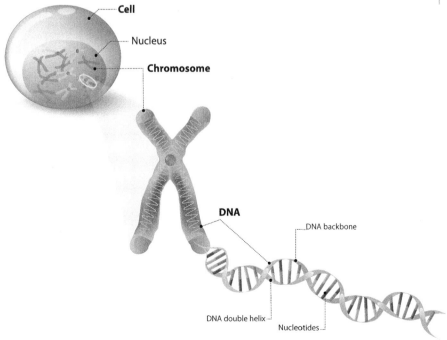

Figure 14.6. DNA chromosome structure.

ISOLATING DNA FROM STRAWBERRIES

DNA is found within the cell nucleus. The supercoiled DNA is protected from the cell environment by a nuclear envelope made up of two lipid bilayers: an inner membrane and outer membrane. DNA is also found within other organelles such as the mitochondria.

The entire cell is protected or contained within a cell membrane, which is another lipid bilayer. In plants, such as a strawberry, the entire cell is also enveloped by a rigid cell wall made up of cellulose fibers.

To isolate or extract the DNA from the strawberry we must break down the cell wall, cell membrane, and nuclear membrane to release the DNA without destroying the DNA polymer. We will use detergent to solubilize the cell membrane. Detergents are partially hydrophobic and partially hydrophilic. The detergent moves into the cell membrane, disrupting the bilayer and releasing the cell's contents. The binding proteins associated with DNA also must be denatured (unfolded) to isolate the DNA.

Isolation of DNA involves three basic steps:

1. **Cell Disruption/Homogenization**: To release the DNA from the nuclei of the strawberry cell, the cell walls, cell membranes, and nuclear membranes must first be broken down. This is done by breaking up and mashing the strawberries to disrupt the cell tissues. To solubilize lipid membranes and denature proteins, a homogenizing medium (Dawn dishwashing liquid and NaCl) is added. The resultant mixture is referred to as the homogenate.

2. **Deproteinization**: The cell's protein must be precipitated, separating it from the DNA that will remain in solution. There are also DNA binding proteins that must be stripped from the DNA. The homogenizing medium includes NaCl, which denatures and precipitates these proteins. The protein and cell debris is removed from the homogenate mechanically (i.e. by filtration through cheesecloth).

3. **Precipitation of DNA**: When ice-cold 2-propanol is added to the homogenate, all components of the homogenate stay in solution except DNA, which precipitates at the interface of the alcohol and homogenate layers.

DISCHE REACTION

The Dische test can be used to qualitatively or quantitatively test for DNA by observing a change in color. A strong acid (sulfuric acid) and heat hydrolyzes (breaks down) the nucleic acids into their individual sugars, bases, and phosphoric acid. The Dische reagent then reacts with the deoxyribose sugars, like that contained in DNA, to form a blue complex.

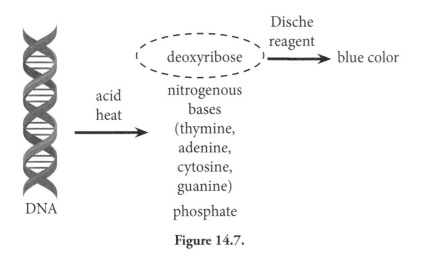

Figure 14.7.

PROCEDURE

WARNING: 2-propanol is very flammable. Keep all containers of 2-propanol closed or covered using a watch glass. All work must be completed within a student bench hood. These hoods are located in the cabinets below the main hoods. Set this bench hood within the metal frame around the exhaust grill on the lab bench at your workstation. Check to make sure that air is being drawn through this hood before beginning your work by holding a Kimwipe against the air vent. All steps in the procedure that involve 2-propanol should be performed in the student bench hood.

▶ EATING IS STRICTLY FORBIDDEN IN THE LABORATORY.

PART I. ANALYSIS OF FAT CONTENT IN POTATO CHIPS

In this part of the experiment, you will determine the fat content in two types of Ruffles potato chips – baked and original – and compare your results to the fat content listed on the nutritional labels. For each type of chip, record the serving size (mass) and total fat per serving (mass) from the package label in your lab notebook.

Extraction and Filtration

Label two clean, dry 250-mL beakers with the types of potato chips that you will analyze: original and baked. Weigh each 250-mL beaker on a balance and record the mass to two places beyond the decimal point (0.01 g). Add about 7 g of potato chips to each beaker and record the mass of the beaker + chips to two places beyond the decimal point.

Gently break up the chips with a metal spatula. Crush the chips until the pieces are about 5 mm.

Obtain about 120 mL of room temperature 2-propanol in a 250-mL beaker. Add 25 mL of 2-propanol to each beaker and stir for 1 minute. Cover each beaker with a watch glass and let them stand for 10 minutes, stirring every 2 minutes.

In the meantime, place boiling beads into two clean, dry 100-mL beakers. Label the beakers appropriately and weigh each beaker + beads to three places beyond the decimal point (0.001 g). Record the mass of each beaker + beads.

Set up 2 separate ring stands and filtration apparatus to filter the 2 samples—the extract from the baked chips and the extract from the regular chips.

Place a funnel in a ring stand above each 100-mL beaker as shown in Figure 14.8 and described below.

- Make sure that the bottom of the funnel is inside the beaker, but is not so low that it will touch the extract.

- Fold a piece of filter paper in half, then in half again (it should be in quarters now).

- Pull apart the filter paper so that one layer of filter paper is on one side and three are on the other. This should make a cone shape.

- Slide your filter paper cone into your glass funnel.

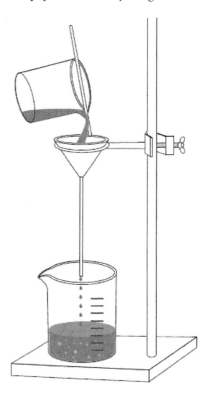

Figure 14.8. Using a funnel for gravity filtration.

Use the technique illustrated above and described below to slowly pour the 2-propanol/fat extract through the filter paper. Keep the beaker covered with a watch glass when not pouring to contain the 2-propanol fumes.

- Place a clean, dry glass stirring rod over the beaker, bisecting the spout.

- Place your index finger over the rod to hold it in place and pour the extract down the glass stir rod and into the funnel.

- Pour only the extract, not the chips.

After the extract has been poured off, add another 25 mL of 2-propanol to the potato chips in each beaker. Stir. Allow to sit another 10 minutes, stirring every 2 minutes.

Filter the second portion of 2-propanol/fat extract through the same filtration set-up you used for the first filtration.

Repeat the filtration process with the second sample (i.e. the other type of chips) and second filtration apparatus. Make sure to keep the two types of chips separate from each other.

Removal of solvent and isolation of fat

The fat has a much higher boiling point (about 200°C) than 2-propanol (83°C), so you will boil off the 2-propanol to isolate the fat. When the extract stops boiling, all of the 2-propanol has evaporated.

Set up a hot plate within the student bench hood. Place two white ceramic hot pads beside the hot plate.

Place the 100-mL beakers of extract on the hot plate within a student bench hood. Begin heating the extract at a setting of "6" to boil off the 2-propanol. You must lower the heat setting as the sample begins to boil vigorously so the solution doesn't splatter out of the beaker. You must keep the solution boiling, however, to evaporate all of the 2-propanol. Both sample loss and incomplete evaporation of 2-propanol can affect your recovery results.

▶ CAUTION: Do not leave the beaker unattended. Do not burn the fat!

When the extract has stopped boiling, take the beaker from the hot plate and place it on the heat resistant pad. Allow the samples to cool to room temperature.

Find the mass of the beaker + beads + fat to three places beyond the decimal point.

WASTE DISPOSAL AND CLEANUP

WASH YOUR GLASSWARE IMMEDIATELY WITH HOT, SOAPY WATER.

Dispose of any leftover 2-propanol in the waste jar for propanol.

Filter paper, boiling beads and leftover potato chips can be discarded in the trash barrel.

Keep your safety goggles on until you have cleaned your work area and are leaving lab.

Lock your lab drawer before leaving lab.

DATA ANALYSIS/RESULTS

Based on the serving size and amount of fat per serving found on each potato chip package, calculate the theoretical mass percent of fat contained in each type of potato chip.

Use your results to calculate the experimental mass percent of fat contained in each type of potato chip.

Calculate the percent recovery of fat for each type of potato chip.

DISCUSSION

1. Which chip had the lowest amount of fat? Why is it easier to extract fat from original potato chips? Explain. Support your claim with evidence (i.e. experimental data), and connect your evidence to your claim using reasoning.

2. Discuss sources of error that might have caused your recovery of fat from the potato chips to vary from 100%. Explain your reasoning.

3. Conduct brief online research to answer the question "What are potential health effects if fats are overheated?" Properly cite your source.

PART II. ISOLATION OF DNA FROM STRAWBERRIES

Your group will isolate DNA from strawberries using common household chemicals. The DNA molecule is very fragile, so it is important to follow all instructions carefully. You must wear gloves to prevent the nucleases (DNA degrading enzymes) on your skin from contaminating the glassware and destroying the DNA.

Chill 2-propanol for the DNA precipitation step

Prepare a bucket with about 2 inches of ice in the bottom. Obtain 60 mL of 2-propanol in a 250-mL beaker. Place the 2-propanol on the ice to cool. Stir the propanol occasionally. The propanol needs to be ice cold to successfully precipitate the DNA.

Prepare hot water for the Dische reaction

Prepare a **boiling** water bath. Fill a 100-mL beaker with about 50 mL of deionized water and place it on a hot plate. Adjust the heat setting to 6.

Cell Disruption/Homogenization

Prepare the homogenizing media: To a 250-mL beaker, add 1.5 g NaCl(s), 8 mL of colorless Dawn dishwashing liquid, and 45 mL of deionized water. It is best to measure the dishwashing liquid in a 50-mL graduated cylinder, and then measure the water in the same cylinder to rinse out some of the soap.

Stir the homogenizing medium until the sodium chloride has dissolved and the solution is well mixed.

Obtain three strawberries and remove the green tops. Put three strawberries into a plastic bag, push all the air out and seal the bag tightly. For 2 minutes, squeeze and mash the strawberries with your fingers.

Add the homogenizing solution to the bag. Push all the extra air out of the bag and seal the bag tightly. Squeeze and mash the strawberries with your finger for 1 more minute.

Deproteinization

Prepare to filter the homogenate to remove some of the protein and other plant material. Drape the provided piece of cheesecloth over a clean 600-mL beaker and secure the cloth with a rubber band, as shown in Figure 14.9. Pour the homogenate into the middle of the cheesecloth.

Figure 14.9. Set-up for filtration through cheesecloth.

Allow the homogenate to filter through the cheesecloth for 10 minutes, then gather the sides of the cheesecloth into a bundle and discard the cheesecloth and excess strawberry material in the trash.

Record your observations in your laboratory notebook.

Precipitation of DNA

Pour 30 mL of your filtered homogenate into a clean 100-mL beaker. Measure 50 mL of your iced 2-propanol in a 50-mL graduated cylinder. Tilt the beaker of homogenate and very slowly pour the cold propanol down the side of the beaker. The alcohol should form a one-inch deep layer on top of the homogenate. Do not allow the propanol and homogenate to mix. The DNA is insoluble in propanol and will precipitate at the interface of the two liquids.

Record your observations in your laboratory notebook.

Spool or wind the stringy DNA onto a small glass rod by rotating the rod in one direction at the interface of the two solutions in the beaker.

Put the small glass rod with the DNA sample into a small test tube and label the test tube "DNA".

You will use this sample for the Dische reaction test.

Do not dispose of the homogenate until you have tested your sample for deoxyribose with the Dische reaction. You may need some DNA for duplicate tests.

The Dische Reaction: Testing for Deoxyribose in DNA

Label a small test tube "C" for a control solution that contains no DNA.

Place 20 drops of 2 M sulfuric acid, H_2SO_4, in each test tube ("DNA" and "C") and mix the solutions.

Put the two test tubes in a boiling water bath for 15 minutes.

Remove the test tubes from the bath and allow them to cool for 5 minutes.

Carefully add 40 drops of Dische reagent to each test tube, and then stir to mix.

Put the tubes back into the boiling water bath and heat the bath to boiling again.

Boil for 5 additional minutes.

Remove the test tubes from the bath and allow them to cool for room temperature.

Observe the contents of each test tube and compare to the picture of positive and negative tests for DNA posted in your laboratory. Record your observations and conclusions in your notebook.

WASTE DISPOSAL AND CLEANUP

Dispose of the contents in the "Waste Jar for Dische Test Solutions."

The leftover strawberry homogenate/propanol mix may be poured down the drain with plenty of water.

Any unused propanol can be disposed of in the "Waste Jar for Propanol."

DATA ANALYSIS/RESULTS

Summarize the identities and amounts of chemicals or substances used in Part II.

Describe your observations for the Deproteinization and DNA precipitation steps.

Summarize the procedure, observations and results of the Dische test.

DISCUSSION

1. In this experiment, we spooled DNA on a rod. What structural characteristic(s) give(s) us the ability to spool the DNA?

2. What was the purpose of adding salt to the homogenization solution? Explain in your own words.

3. Why is it easy to isolate DNA from strawberries? Why is it harder to extract human DNA? Explain. Provide an appropriate reference to any sources you consult.

4. When you look at the structure of DNA, what are the reasons DNA can be collected at the interface of both solutions? Draw a picture if that helps you explain your answer.

Title: _____

Work Done and Report Prepared by: _____

Date: _____ Lab Section Number: _____

GOAL *(for both parts)*

PART I: ANALYSIS OF FAT CONTENT IN POTATO CHIPS
DATA/DATA ANALYSIS/RESULTS

	Potato Chips	
	Original	Baked
Mass of 250-mL beaker		
Mass of 250-mL beaker and potato chips		
Mass of potato chips		
Mass of 100-mL beaker and boiling beads		
Mass of 100-mL beaker, boiling beads and extracted fat		
Mass of extracted fat		
Mass of one serving (from package)		
Mass of fat per serving (from package)		
Theoretical mass percent of fat		
Experimental mass percent of fat		
Percent recovery		

Sample calculations for (1) theoretical mass percent of fat, (2) experimental mass percent of fat and (3) percent recovery for the original *or* baked potato chips: (show your work and units)

DISCUSSION

Answer the discussion questions found in the laboratory manual. Attach additional paper if needed.

PART II: ISOLATION OF DNA FROM STRAWBERRIES

DATA

Procedure: Summarize the identities and amounts of chemicals or substances used in Part II.

Chemical or substance name	Amount	Physical Description	Purpose of chemical or substance (Why did you use it?)

Observations: Describe your observations for each part of the procedure listed below.

DATA ANALYSIS/RESULTS

Summarize the Dische test and results in the table below.

Test tube	Test tube contents (list)	Description of test tube contents after addition of Dische reagent and heating	Dische test results (positive or negative)

DISCUSSION

Answer the discussion questions found in the laboratory manual. Attach additional paper as needed.

THE ANALYTICAL BALANCE

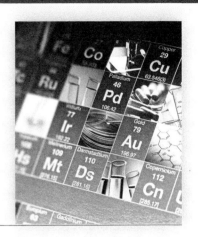

In the Purdue General Chemistry Laboratories, there are two types of balances: milligram balances in the main lab room weigh to the nearest 0.001 g and analytical balances in the balance room which weigh to the nearest 0.0001g. Make sure you record the number of digits appropriate for the balance you are using.

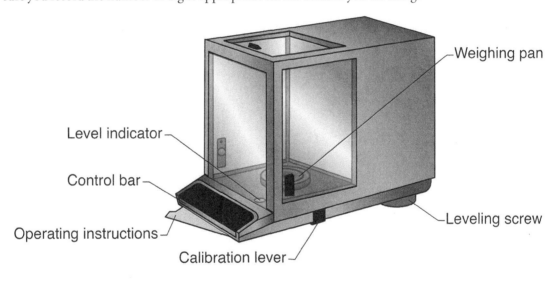

Check the leveling bubble on the floor of the weighing chamber. If the bubble is centered, go to the next step. Center the leveling bubble by turning the leveling screws on the bottom and toward the rear of the balance.

TURNING ON THE BALANCE

Close all weighing chamber doors and briefly press the control bar on the front of the balance or press the "ON" button. Within a few seconds, the balance will display a set of zeros. If zeros do not appear in all the digits, press the control bar again.

WEIGHING A LIQUID, POWDER, OR GRANULAR SUBSTANCE

Always weigh these substances using a weighing container provided in the lab! Place this container on the balance pan. Close the chamber doors. Press the control bar briefly; the display changes to zero. This is referred to as "taring" the balance. Next, add the substance up to the desired weight. Add the solid to the weighing container a small amount at a time until you have a feel for how much the solid weighs. Then you can adjust your addition rate until you reach the desired weight. Be careful not to spill chemicals on the balance. Close the chamber doors to get an accurate reading.

WEIGHING A SOLID OBJECT DIRECTLY ON THE BALANCE

When it is necessary to weigh a solid object (a metal cylinder, for example) directly on the balance, tare the balance and then carefully place the object on the pan and close all the chamber doors. The display will show you the mass of the object.

CLEANING UP

Make sure that all chemicals spilled on the balance are wiped up immediately. When in doubt, check with your graduate instructor!

TURNING THE BALANCE OFF
(DONE ONLY AT THE END OF THE DAY)

To turn the balance off, lift up gently on the control bar or press the off button until the display goes dark.

▶ If the balance does not seem to be operating properly, tell your instructor, then go to the storeroom and report the problem.

APPENDIX B

VOLUMETRIC MEASUREMENT TECHNIQUES

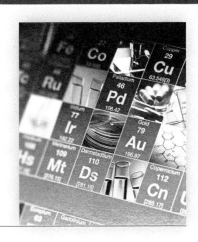

INTRODUCTION

One of the most common measurements in the chemical laboratory is measuring the volume of a liquid. Solutions are often used and transferred from one container to another. In some cases, it is important to accurately know the amount of liquid transferred. In this and future chemistry labs, you will come into contact with various pieces of laboratory glassware. Each of these has a specific purpose and a distinct level of accuracy and precision associated with it.

Beakers and Erlenmeyer flasks are used for holding solutions, mixing reagents, carrying out chemical reactions, or crudely measuring volumes of liquids. The graduated markings on a beaker or Erlenmeyer flask are only approximate (~5%, ~2 significant figures), so they should not be used for accurate volume measurements.

Graduated cylinders are designed to measure liquid volumes with moderate accuracy (~0.5%, ~3 significant figures). The tall, narrow column makes for a more precise reading of the liquid level. For accurate volume measurement, choose the smallest graduated cylinder that can measure that volume. Increment markings on graduated cylinders vary based on the volume of the cylinder.

The greatest accuracy and precision (±0.05%, ~4 significant figures) is obtained with analytical glassware, such as **volumetric pipets, burets,** and **volumetric flasks**. Volumetric pipets are designed to accurately deliver a fixed volume of solution. Burets are used for the accurate measurement of a variable amount of a solution, primarily in titrations. Volumetric flasks are designed to accurately contain a fixed volume of solution and are generally used for solution preparation so that a solute can be diluted to a known, accurate volume.

When recording measurements in the lab, it is important that you note the uncertainty of the different measuring devices and record the appropriate number of significant figures. To properly record the uncertainty in a measurement, the value should use all of the known digits *plus* one estimated digit. In the lab, you will make a judgment on the value of the last digit in a measurement. For example, the burets we use in lab are calibrated in divisions of 0.1 mL, so you should estimate the final digit and report the volume to the nearest 0.01 mL. Many glassware manufacturers note the tolerance (uncertainty in the accuracy of a device) on the measuring device itself.

Good volumetric techniques are a critical part of accurate and precise measurements in chemistry and other scientific fields.

The detailed information that follows is intended to help you achieve two main goals with regard to using volumetric measuring techniques in an analysis procedure:

1. Avoid doing anything to change the concentration of the component of interest in the solution from which an aliquot is taken or in the aliquot itself.

2. Measure aliquots accurately and make dilutions carefully.

Standard Solution

A **standard solution** is one for which the composition is known or fixed with a given level of uncertainty. Standard solutions require very careful preparation because concentration of standards is used to determine the concentration of unknown solutions or calibrate instruments.

For example, if we were to dissolve exactly 1.3421 grams of pure sodium carbonate (Na_2CO_3, 105.99 g/mol) in pure water and then dilute the solution to exactly 100.0 mL in a 100-mL volumetric flask with pure water, then we would have a standard solution of sodium carbonate with a concentration of 0.1267 mol/L.

$$\frac{1.3421\,g\,Na_2CO_3 \times \dfrac{1\,mol\,Na_2CO_3}{105.99\,g}}{0.100\,L\,solution} = \frac{0.1267\,mol\,Na_2CO_3}{L} = 0.1267\,M\,Na_2CO_3$$

Unknown Solution

In **quantitative** lab work, an unknown solution is one for which the composition of one or more substances is not known to the desired degree of uncertainty. For example, it is generally recognized that ordinary vinegar contains about 5% acetic acid. However, vinegar would be considered an unknown solution if we needed to know the concentration of acetic acid to three significant figures.

Stock Solution

A stock solution refers to the larger volume of solution from which you will take portions needed for the measurements. To avoid contamination, never dip anything such as a pipet into the stock solution. Always pour an amount of the solution which is slightly more than the amount needed into a small, clean, dry beaker. Never pour unused solution back into the stock solution.

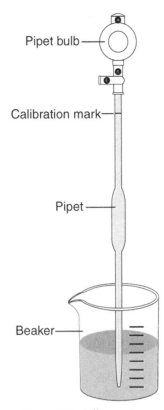

Figure B.1. Filling a pipet.

Aliquot

An **aliquot** is a measured fraction of a sample such as a standard solution, stock solution, or unknown solution. For example, if we were to measure a 25.00 mL sample from 1.0 L of a standard or unknown solution, the 25.00 mL sample would be called an aliquot of the sample. Two 25.00 mL samples would be two aliquots.

Measuring Aliquots of Solution

The two tools you will use to measure aliquots of solutions are pipets and burets.

Using a Pipet to Measure Liquid Volumes

! WARNING! Pipets work very much like straws. However, do not ever use your mouth to pull liquid into a pipet. This is the most common method of becoming poisoned in a chemical laboratory or becoming infected in a clinical laboratory. Mouth pipetting is forbidden in the chemistry department.

Cleaning and Rinsing Pipets

Pipets should first be rinsed at least once with the stock solution. The purpose of the rinse is to wet the inside walls of the pipet and remove any other solution left behind by previous use. Use a bulb (see directions below) to draw a small volume of the stock solution into the pipet and thoroughly wet the interior surface by tilting and rotating the pipet. Discard the rinse solution down the drain or into the appropriate waste container.

Filling and Delivering a Sample Using a Pipet

Collapse the bulb for aspiration by squeezing the A valve at the top of the bulb with your thumb and forefinger while squeezing the bulb into your palm with your remaining fingers. Release the valve. Holding the pipet about 2 cm from the top, gently insert the pipet into the bulb using a slight twisting motion. Do not force the pipet into the bulb; ½ cm is sufficient to make a seal between the bulb and pipet.

Place the tip of the pipet in the liquid that you wish to dispense. To pull liquid into the pipet, squeeze the S valve until the liquid rises above the desired calibration mark. Wipe the outside of the pipet stem with a lint-free tissue.

With the calibration mark at eye level, gently squeeze the E valve on the side arm of the bulb to allow the bottom of the meniscus to line up with the desired calibration mark. Tap the tip of the pipet to the side of the vessel to remove any drops from the tip.

To dispense the liquid, squeeze the E valve on the side arm of the bulb.

If you are using a graduated pipet, allow the liquid to flow to the desired mark. If you are using a volumetric pipet, allow the liquid to flow freely until it stops. When the desired volume has been dispensed, touch the tip of the pipet to the inside of the vessel to remove any droplets that may remain. DO NOT BLOW OR FORCE ANY REMAINING LIQUID FROM THE PIPET. The volumetric pipets are calibrated "to deliver" and this takes into account the fact that a small amount of liquid remains in the tip.

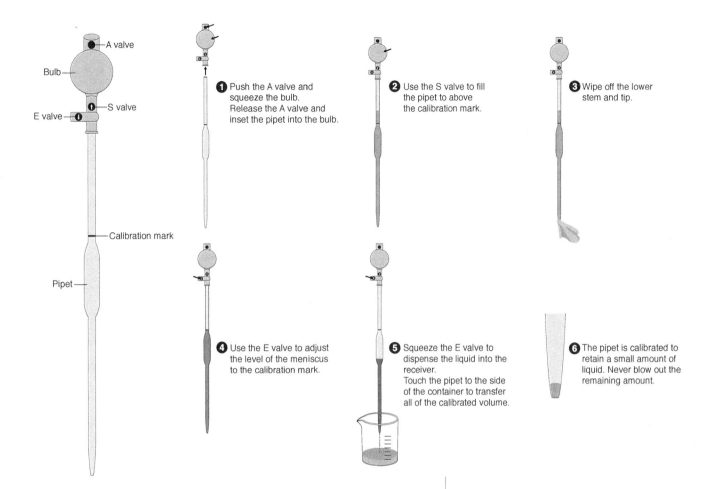

Figure B.3. Using a pipet.

Using a Buret to Measure Liquid Volumes

Cleaning

Assume that burets in the general chemistry lab need to be cleaned and rinsed well with deionized water before using.

The buret should be rinsed twice with a small amount of the reagent it is to hold before loading. The rinses must be disposed of in the proper manner.

Support

Special buret clamps are used to hold and support a buret to a ring stand during use. These clamps come in several shapes.

Filling a Buret

- Close the stopcock, and then tilt the buret slightly to one side and pour the liquid from a beaker slowly down the inside wall of the buret to avoid forming air bubbles in the liquid.

- Place a beaker under the tip of the buret and open the stopcock part way, permitting liquid to flow slowly until the buret tip is completely filled with liquid.

- If any air bubbles are present in the stopcock or buret tip, open the stopcock full in an effort to force them out. Repeat as necessary.

- Once air is removed from the stopcock and tip, fill the buret until the top of the liquid level is in the calibrated range of the buret.

- Touch the inside wall of a clean beaker to the buret tip one time.

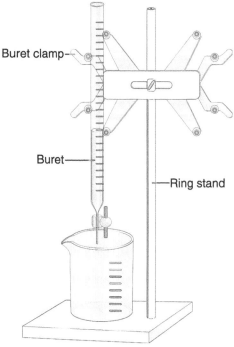

Buret clamp

Buret

Ring stand

Figure B.4. Buret setup.

Reading a Buret

Note that the numerical scale on a buret is designed to measure the amount of liquid delivered or drained—*NOT* the amount in the buret.

- After filling, wait a few seconds and then record the buret reading at the bottom of the meniscus. You may wish to use a 3 **x** 5 card with a black mark on it. Hold the black mark "behind" the buret so that it is just visible under the meniscus. This will darken the meniscus and make it easier to see against the white card.

- To avoid a parallax error, your eye must be level with the meniscus, and the buret vertical.

The buret should be read to the nearest **0.01 mL**. Since the markings only occur every 0.1 mL, this requires estimating the reading to the nearest 0.01 mL.

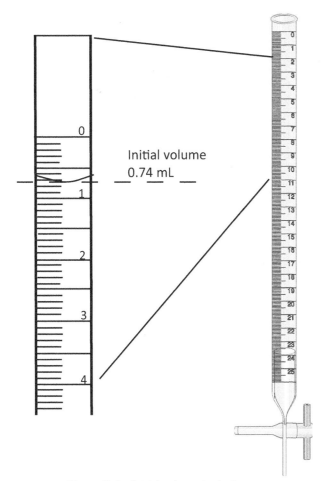

Initial volume
0.74 mL

Figure B.5. Initial volume in the buret.

Titrating with a Buret

Although you may initially find it awkward, a right-handed person should use their left hand to operate the stopcock. To do this, wrap your left hand around the buret and move the stopcock by opposing pressure with your fingers and thumb. This leaves your dominant hand to swirl the flask. All titrating is done with the flask being swirled continuously to ensure the liquid added is well mixed with the solution in the flask.

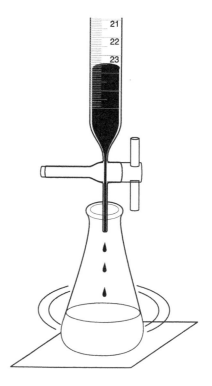

Figure B.6. Delivery of liquid from a buret.

Put the container into which liquid is to be dispensed under the buret tip and open the stopcock part way, permitting fluid to flow slowly into the container, until the desired volume has been dispensed. Wait a few seconds and record the buret reading at the bottom of the meniscus. The volume dispensed is the difference between the final and initial buret readings.

Always perform a "scout" titration. The purpose is to roughly determine what volume of solution is required to reach the endpoint. To do this, open the stopcock so that the solution drains quickly into the flask. Close the stopcock as soon as you notice the color change. You will most likely miss the endpoint. Record the volume of the titrant in your notebook. Remember to subtract the initial buret volume.

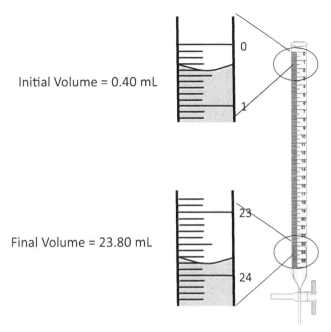

Figure B.7. Reading a buret.

For a more careful titration, open the stopcock just as if you were performing a scout titration. However, stop 0.50 mL–1 mL before the volume expected for the endpoint. Now adjust the stopcock so the solution flows from the buret one drop at a time. An experienced analyst is capable of forming a fractional drop at the tip of the buret and transferring it to the flask by washing the tip with deionized water from a wash bottle or by tapping the flask against the tip. This is done often because one drop contains about 0.05 mL and the buret can be read to 0.01 mL.

If you are using an indicator for the first time and are not familiar with the color change, it might be wise to write down the volume the first time you think the color corresponds to the endpoint. Then add another drop to see how the color changes. If it looks more like the endpoint, again read the buret and write the volume in your notebook. Continue until you are convinced the endpoint has been reached or passed.

Sources of Error

Air bubbles—Air bubbles in the stopcock or buret tips will result in an error in the volume dispensed from the buret.

Improper cleaning—Drops of liquid or bubbles will form on the inside of the buret if the buret is contaminated with other reagents and will result in an error in the volume dispensed

Parallax—Keep your eye level with the meniscus when reading the volume of the buret.

Over or underestimating the endpoint color—titration to an incorrect color.

Slow titration/stirring too vigorously/breathing into the flask—Some solutions are unstable and the titration must be performed quickly. Gases in the air such as carbon dioxide may react with the solution in your flask

Cleanup

Clean the buret as soon as practical after using it with several rinses of deionized water and return it to the proper location so it doesn't get broken. Burets are not cheap and you will have to pay for one if it breaks.

Volumetric Flasks

A special type of glassware called a volumetric flask is used to prepare accurate dilutions of standard and unknown solutions. The volumetric flask has a long thin neck with a calibration mark on it so that solutions can be diluted exactly to the mark.

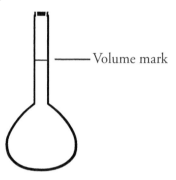

Figure B.8. Volumetric flask.

Note that there may be three lines on the 50-mL plastic volumetric flasks. The middle line represents 50.0 mL.

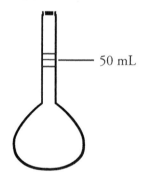

Figure B.9. Plastic volumetric flask.

Before using a volumetric flask, wash with detergent solution and rinse several times with tap water, followed with a minimum of three deionized water rinses.

Make sure that all parts of the inside surface are rinsed.

After cleaning and rinsing, measure the aliquot of solution into the flask using a pipet or buret as described previously. If instructions describe the addition of one or more other reagents, then add those reagents at this time.

After all reagents have been added, carefully add deionized water from a clean dropper pipet or medicine dropper until the liquid meniscus is lined **exactly** with the calibration marking on the neck of the flask.

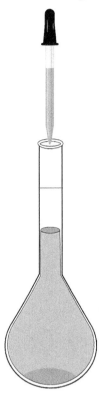

Figure B.10. Filling a volumetric flask.

Volumetric flasks should be closed with Parafilm, thumb put over the Parafilm, and flask inverted for adequate mixing. Because the neck of the flask is long and narrow, several inversions are necessary to achieve good mixing.

Mixing Solutions

Before you pour a small amount of solution into a small, clean, dry beaker to measure aliquots, always mix the solution thoroughly to ensure that any solvent that may have evaporated and condensed on the inside surface is remixed with the solution.

Dilution Factor

The **dilution factor** is the degree to which a sample has been diluted. For example, if we were to take a 25.00 mL sample of vinegar and dilute it to 1000 mL, the dilution factor would be 1000 mL/25 mL, corresponding to a 40-fold dilution of the vinegar sample. Stated differently, the concentration of acetic acid in the diluted sample would be one-fortieth (1/40) that of the original sample, or the original sample is 40 times more concentrated than the diluted sample.

SPECTROSCOPY: AN INTRODUCTION

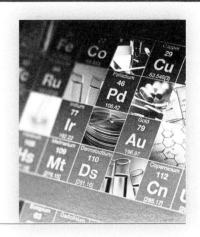

Spectrophotometry is an analytical method based on measuring the amount of light absorbed by a substance. Each compound may absorb or transmit light differently at different wavelengths. The amount of light absorbed depends on the molecule involved and the concentration of these molecules, and can be used to determine the amount of a chemical substance. Spectrophotometry is useful method of quantitative analysis in various fields such as chemistry, physics, biochemistry, pharmaceuticals, and clinical applications.

A spectrophotometer measures the percent of incident light a sample transmits, the percent transmission (%T). The more light a sample absorbs, the smaller the percent transmission. The basic operating components of a spectrophotometer are diagrammed in Figure C.1, where P_0 is the intensity (brightness) of the light entering the cuvet. P is the intensity of the light that passes through the cuvet and sample, and is detected by the spectrophotometer. This is quantified as percent transmittance, %T and can be expressed with the equation:

$$\%T = 100 * (P / P_0).$$

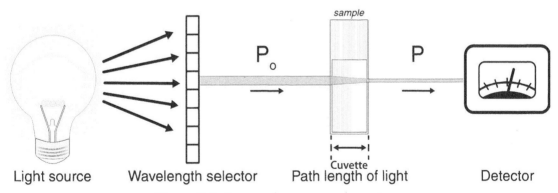

Figure C.1. Spectrophotometer schematic.

Another measure of light absorbed by a sample is the absorbance, A, where:

$$A = -\log P/P_0 \text{ or } -\log (\%T/100).$$

Absorbance is commonly used in spectroscopy because it is proportional to the concentration of the absorbing molecule. The absorbance is also proportional to the path length of light through the sample. The relationship between absorbance at a given wavelength and concentration and path length can be expressed as:

$$\text{absorbance} = (\text{molar absorptivity}) \times \left(\begin{array}{c} \text{path length of light} \\ \text{through the sample} \end{array} \right) \times (\text{concentration})$$

$$A = \varepsilon \times l \times C$$

This relationship is known as the Beer-Lambert Law. The molar absorptivity, ε, is a measure of how strongly a chemical substance absorbs light at a given wavelength, and is an intrinsic property of the substance.

Absorption Spectra and Finding the Wavelength of Maximum Absorption

The plot of a compound's absorbance of light at various wavelengths is called its **absorption spectrum** (horizontal axis = wavelength, vertical axis = absorbance). The plot below shows the absorption spectrum of yellow, red, and blue food dye.

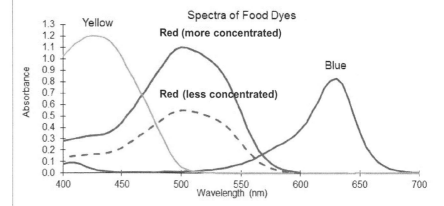

Figure C.2. Absorption spectra of some food dyes.

For quantitative measurements, it is preferable to choose a wavelength of light that is near the maximum absorbance, λ_{max}, for the compound of interest. For example, the λ_{max} of red food dye is approximately 500 nm.

The choice of wavelength for making absorbance measurements is important, and there are two reasons we generally select the wavelength of maximum absorbance (λ_{max}) for a given compound and use it for absorbance measurements.

1. It is where the change in absorbance is greatest for a change in concentration. That is, the measurement of absorbance (concentration) is most sensitive at this wavelength

2. It is where the change in absorbance is least for a slight change in the wavelength. That is, the absorbance will be less sensitive to any error in the spectrophotometer selection of the wavelength. Suppose that a wavelength of 550 nm was chosen for the measurement of Red food dye. This measurement is on the steep portion of the curve, where a small change in the wavelength would cause a large change in the absorbance. Using the wavelength maximum of 500 nm, which has a relative flat profile, will minimize the error in the absorbance if there is a slight error in the wavelength.

Limits of Spectrophotometers

A spectrophotometer has limitations in the maximum absorbance it can measure accurately, so the concentration of the solutions must be chosen so the absorbance measurements are within the linear or working range of the instrument (typically less than 1.5).

The following graph illustrates absorbance data obtained over a wide range of concentrations. As the concentration increases, the measured absorbance levels off because the amount of light transmitted through the sample is now so small that the instrument can no longer detect any difference in absorbance. The region of concentrations chosen for the standard solutions and samples must be below the point where the curve deviates from a straight line. If a sample concentration is outside this range, it must be diluted until the concentration is within the range of the standard concentrations.

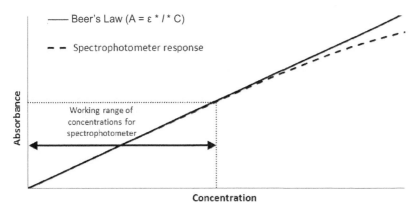

Figure C.3. Linear or working range of the spectrophotometer.

Calibration Plot

The molar absorptivity of a molecule can vary as a function of wavelength, temperature, solvent, pH, and other chemical conditions, so if the conditions of your sample don't match those with which the molar absorptivity was determined, the calculated concentration won't be accurate. Also, spectrometers are not identical and may not necessarily give identical results or even the same results on different days.

A **calibration plot** is a necessary part of determining the concentrations of substances using spectroscopy. A calibration plot is a graph of known data (absorbance vs. concentration) that is used to determine the unknown concentration of a substance in a solution. Several solutions are prepared with known concentrations of the substance of interest and are called **standards** or **standard solutions** and are the independent variable. The measured property, absorbance at a selected wavelength, is the dependent variable.

Molar absorptivity, ε, is a proportionality constant and is an intrinsic property of a species. Therefore, in a graph of absorbance vs. concentration of standard solutions, the slope of the best fit line or trendline is equal to the molar absorptivity of that substance at a given wavelength and path length of light through the sample (see Figure C.4 below).

When you know the molar absorptivity of the substance of interest and the absorbance of the solution, you can calculate the concentration of the substance of interest in the solution.

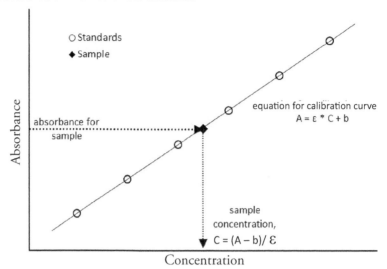

Figure C.4. Interpreting a calibration plot: absorbance vs. concentration

The Blank Solution

The solvent, cuvet material or solutes other than the compound of interest may also absorb light. These interferences can be corrected for by filling a cuvet with a solution containing all the components except for the absorbing species of interest. This is referred to as a **blank solution**. Setting the spectrophotometer to "0" absorbance with the blank solution instructs the instrument to subtract the absorbance due to blank from the absorbance of future samples. An analogy is the taring of a balance to subtract the weight of the empty container.

Summary

Measurement and analysis procedures of spectrometry include:

1. determination of an appropriate wavelength to make absorbance measurements

2. measurement of absorbance of standards using a spectrophotometer

3. construction of a calibration plot (absorbance vs. concentration):

   a. to obtain the equation of the best fit straight line through the data points

   b. to obtain the molar absorptivity from the equation of the straight calibration line

4. measure absorbance of unknown solution and use calibration plot to determination its concentration

Cuvets

Cuvets hold the sample that is to be inserted into a spectrophotometer for measurement. Cuvets may be made of plastic or glass and may be rectangular or cylindrical. Glass cuvets are **NOT** test tubes. Cuvets are manufactured more carefully for optical clarity than test tubes and are, therefore, more expensive. To make measurements of solutions accurately, the following procedures need to be followed.

- Handle cuvets with care to avoid scratching or damaging them. Never use a test tube brush to clean a cuvette. *(Scratches scatter light!)*

- Use the same cuvet for all measurements unless you have a set of precisely matched cuvets.

- Rinse the cuvet first with deionized water and then twice with a small amount (~1 mL) of solution that is to be measured. "Roll" the solution in the cuvette so all the inside surface is rinsed. Empty all rinses into a beaker that is being used as a waste container.

- Start measurements with the lowest concentration, then progress to the highest concentration. Empty solution from the cuvet into the waste container, rinse with the next more concentrated solution, then fill cuvet with solution.

- Plastic cuvets need to be about ¾ full for measurements. Glass cuvettes need to be about ½ full.

- Make sure there are no bubbles in the solution to be measured. *(Bubbles refract light!)*

- Clean the outside of the cuvette with an absorbent, lint-free, soft tissue such as KimWipes or AccuWipes. *(Fingerprints absorb and scatter light!)*

- Insert the cuvet into the sample compartment or sample holder the same way each time. Most cuvets have a mark to help orient it the same way each time.

Using the Vernier SpectroVis Plus™ Spectrophotometer

Figure C.5. The Vernier SpectroVis Plus™ spectrophotometer

Connect the SpectroVis Pro to the Computer

- Connect the SpectoVis spectrophotometer to the computer with a USB cable.

- Start the Logger Pro application.

Set the SpectroVis Plus to Zero

- Prepare a blank solution

- Rinse and fill a cuvet about ¾ full with the blank solution. Wipe the outside of the cuvet with a KimWipe.

- From the **Experiment** menu, choose **Calibrate>Spectophotometer:1**

- Wait. The calibration dialog box will pop-up and count down time needed for lamp to warm up.

- When the warm up is complete, place the cuvet with the blank in the sample chamber of the SpectroVis.

- Click **Finish Calibration**.

- Click **OK**.

Collecting a Spectrum (Absorbance vs Wavelength) of Sample to Find the Wavelength of Maximum Absorption.

- Click on the **Configure Spectrometer** button, ▮▮, also known as "Rainbow Mtn."

- Select **Absorbance vs. Wavelength** as the Collection Mode.

- Rinse and fill a cuvet about ¾ full with one of the standards. Wipe the outside of the cuvet with a KimWipe.

- Place the cuvet in the sample chamber of the SpectroVis.

- Click ▶ Collect .

- Wait 10 seconds.

- Click ▢ Stop, to end data collection.

- Press **Autoscale**, $\boxed{\text{A}}$, for a better representation of the spectra.

Collecting Data for a Calibration Plot (Absorbance vs Concentration)

- Click on **Configure Spectrometer**, 🏭

- Select **Absorbance vs. Concentration** as the **Collection Mode**. NOTE: Logger Pro has chosen the wavelength of maximum absorbance, λ_{max}, for you.

- Change the **Column Name** to Concentration, the **Short Name** to conc, and the **Units** to mol/L.

- Click **OK**

- Measure the standards from the least concentrated to the most concentrated:

  1. Rinse the cuvette with a small amount of the standard solution by rolling the solution in the cuvette. Discard the rinse into a waste beaker.

  2. Fill the cuvette about ¾ full with the standard solution.

  3. Insert the cuvette into the spectrophotometer. Press **Collect**.

  4. Wait 10 seconds, press 🌀 Keep. Enter the concentration. NOTE: A value in scientific notation such as 1.00×10^{-3} must be entered as 1.00E-3. Press **OK**.

  5. Repeat with other standards.

- Click **Stop** to end data collection.

STUDENT NOTES

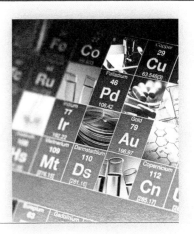

FILTRATION

Filtration is a technique used for two main purposes. The first purpose is to remove solid impurities from a liquid. The second purpose is to collect a desired solid from a solution where it was precipitated or crystallized. The two general filtration methods are gravity filtration and vacuum filtration.

Gravity filtration uses gravity to draw a solution through a paper filter or other solid medium held in a funnel. It is often used to remove solid impurities from a solution. Gravity filtration can be used when the force of gravity alone is sufficient to pull the liquid through the solid medium.

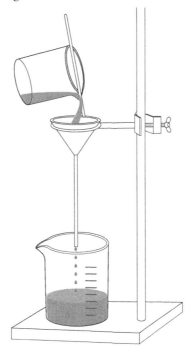

To perform a gravity filtration:

1. Rest the funnel in a triangle supported by a ring on a ring stand, and set a beaker underneath the funnel.

2. Fold the filter paper in half, and then in half again. Open the filter paper into a cone, place the filter paper cone in the funnel, and moisten the paper with a few milliliters of the solvent used (usually water). The moistened filter paper should help keep it in place for the filtration. Allow the solvent to pass through the filter paper into the beaker. Once the solvent has stopped draining through the funnel, replace the beaker with a clean one to collect the filtrate.

3. Before filtering, allow the solid in the mixture to settle to the bottom of the container. Carefully pour the liquid into the center of the funnel, being careful not to let the level of liquid rise above the top edge of the filter paper. By initially transferring only the liquid portion of the mixture, the filtration will take less time.

4. Once most of the liquid has passed through the filter, transfer the solid from the container into the funnel. Swirl a few milliliters of solvent with the solid that remains in the original container and quickly (while the solid is still suspended) transfer this mixture to the filtration funnel. Repeat with small portions of solvent until all the solid is transferred to the filter. The volume of the rinses should be minimal so that it does not dissolve too much of the solid or dilute the filtrate too much.

5. Washing the solid is important, whether the solid or filtrate will be collected. If the solid is to be collected, washing will remove any soluble impurities. If the filtrate is to be collected, washing will ensure that all of the solute (the compound that you want that is dissolved in the solvent) is removed from the solid and collected in the filtrate. The volume of the washes should be minimal so that it does not dissolve too much of the solid or dilute the filtrate too much.

Vacuum filtration uses a vacuum to draw a solution through a paper filter. This technique is used when a faster filtration is needed or when the force of gravity alone is not enough to pull the liquid through the filter paper. Vacuum filtration is faster than gravity filtration because the solution is forced through the filter paper by a pressure difference. It is often used to collect solid products resulting from precipitation or crystallization.

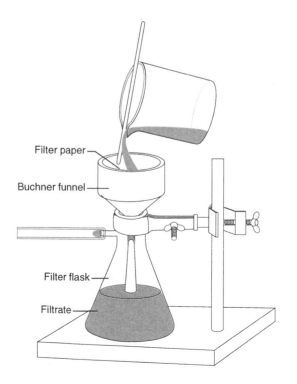

Filter paper

Buchner funnel

Filter flask

Filtrate

A simple way of generating a vacuum in the laboratory is by an apparatus called an aspirator. In an aspirator, water flows through a tapered tube. As the tube narrows, the water's speed increases and its pressure decreases (called the Venturi effect). The vacuum occurs at the sidearm of the aspirator, which can be connected to the sidearm of a filter flask with thick-walled tubing. The water flow should be turned on full for the best vacuum, though the maximum vacuum is limited by the vapor pressure of the water generating the vacuum.

To perform a vacuum filtration

1. Obtain a filter flask, Büchner funnel, rubber funnel adapter, bucket, and thick-walled tubing from the drawers or cabinets in the back of the laboratory. Clamp the filter flask securely to a ring stand with a 3-prong clamp.

2. Connect the rubber tubing to the flask and aspirator. Place a bucket under the aspirator and fill the bucket with water. This helps reduce the splashing when the aspirator water flow is turned on full.

3. Insert a Büchner funnel into the top of the filter flask with a rubber funnel adaptor. Wetting the adaptor can help make the seal airtight.

4. Place the filter paper in the funnel. The filter paper should be small enough to remain flat but large enough to cover all of the holes in the funnel. Wet the filter paper with a small amount of the solvent to be used in the filtration. This will help the filter paper adhere to the bottom and keep solids from passing under the paper during filtration.

5. Turn on the water for the aspirator. The vacuum generated by the aspirator should draw the wet filter paper against the bottom of the funnel, sealing the bottom. You might need to lightly press down on the funnel to help seal around the rubber filter adaptor.

6. Pour the mixture into the center of the filter paper. The vacuum should rapidly pull the liquid through the funnel. Keep the accumulating solid in the center of the filter paper to minimize the chances of the liquid and solid bypassing the filter paper. Rinse the filter cake with a small amount of fresh, cold solvent to help remove impurities that were in the solution.

7. Continue to run the aspirator. This will draw air through the solid, which helps to dry it somewhat.

8. Disconnect the rubber tubing from the flask before turning off the water flow to the aspirator. If the water in the aspirator stops flowing with the tubing still attached to the filter flask, the reduced pressure inside the flask may draw water from inside the aspirator into the filter flask.

STUDENT NOTES

APPENDIX E

USING A
BUNSEN BURNER

The Bunsen burner is a convenient source of heat for the chemical laboratory. A Bunsen burner flame is very hot and is designed to completely combust the gas without producing soot. It can do this because it mixes the gaseous fuel with air before it starts to burn.

The gas needle valve controls the rate at which methane (CH_4) gas enters the burner and determines the size of the flame.

The air vents control the rate at which air enters the burner.

Methane and air mix in the burner barrel and produce a flame whose temperature is determined by the air-to-fuel ratio.

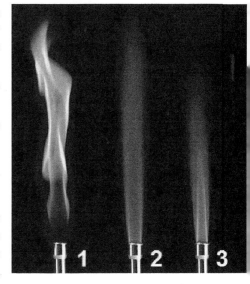

1. Safety or luminous flame (~300°C) A flickering, yellow flame. The flame is visible, and warns of the danger of an ignition source or burn hazard. It is not usually used to heat anything, but to indicate that the burner is on when not in use.
2. Medium or blue flame (~500°C) A light blue, almost invisible flame. This is used for general heating.
3. Hot or working flame (~1000°C) A blue flame with an inner blue cone. The hottest point is at the tip of the inner blue cone.

A blue flame is very hot and is not as easily seen as a yellow flame. To be safe, it is best to turn off the Bunsen burner when not in use.

Glassware should be heated evenly and gradually. Avoid heating glassware directly with a Bunsen burner flame. The focused heat where the flame is applied may not be able to spread evenly into the rest of the glass. The large temperature differential may cause uneven thermal expansion resulting in enough stress to crack the glass. A wire gauze is normally used to help evenly distribute the heat from the flame. Test tubes may be heated directly, but the flame or tube should be continuously moved, to prevent any one portion from being heated too strongly.

When things are heated, they become **<u>HOT</u>** and remain **<u>HOT</u>** for a period of time.

Hot objects look exactly the same as cold objects.

Use caution whenever working with heat or flames—most laboratory burns result from carelessness when handling hot objects.

Glassware needs to cool gradually and evenly. Place the hot glassware on a white fiber pad (found on the reagent bench) instead of placing on the cold bench surface. Set the glassware in a safe place for cooling and indicate with a warning sign that reads "Hot".

IF ANY PROBLEM OCCURS, TURN THE GAS OFF AT THE TAP IMMEDIATELY.

The Bunsen burners can be found in a drawer in the back of the room.

TURNING ON THE BUNSEN BURNER

1. Close the needle valve at the base of the burner.

2. Close the air vents by turning the barrel in the clockwise direction.

3. Make sure the tubing is in good condition and securely connected to the inlet at the base of the burner.

4. Connect the other end of the tubing to the gas nozzle at your lab station. The gas valve should be in the "off" position (valve handle is perpendicular to the nozzle).

5. Remove any flammable or unnecessary items near the burner.

6. Open the needle valve at the base of the burner a half turn.

7. Light a match.

8. Turn the gas valve at the lab station to the "on" position (valve handle is parallel to the nozzle.).

9. Bring the lit match alongside the barrel of the burner and raise it slowly to the top edge of the barrel. Once the burner is lit, extinguish the match with water and discard it in the trash.

10. At this point the flame is yellow and flickering (safety or luminous flame).

11. Turn the barrel of the burner counter-clockwise to open the air vents. As you increase the air vent opening, the flame should become a light blue, almost invisible flame. **<u>CAUTION:</u>** Do not to turn the barrel so far that it detaches from the burner (>10 turns).

12. One can achieve a hotter flame by continuing to increase the air supply until a blue inner cone appears. The hottest point is at the tip of the inner blue cone.

13. Adjust the needle valve of the burner to achieve the desired flame height. **<u>CAUTION:</u>** The valve can fall out if turned too far (>10 turns). You may also need to adjust the air vent as you increase or decrease the gas flow.

TURNING OFF THE BUNSEN BURNER

1. Close the gas valve at your lab bench to the "off" position.

2. Allow the burner to cool.

3. If you are finished using the Bunsen burner, disconnect the hose from the gas nozzle on the lab bench, and return the Bunsen burner to the drawer in the back of the room.

Exp. Number	Experiment Title/ Subject			1
Name		Lab Partner	Course	Section

Student's Signature	Date	Instructor/TA Signature	Date

1

Exp. Number	Experiment Title/ Subject			1
Name		Lab Partner	Course	Section

Student's Signature	Date	Instructor/TA Signature	Date

Exp. Number	Experiment Title/ Subject			2
Name		Lab Partner	Course	Section

Student's Signature	Date	Instructor/TA Signature	Date

Note: Insert Foldover Back flap under each copy set before writing

Exp. Number	Experiment Title/ Subject			2
Name		Lab Partner	Course	Section

Student's Signature	Date	Instructor/TA Signature	Date

Note: Insert Foldover Back flap under each copy set before writing

FOUNTAINHEAD PRESS

Exp. Number	Experiment Title/ Subject			3
Name		Lab Partner	Course	Section

Student's Signature	Date	Instructor/TA Signature	Date

Note: Insert Foldover Back flap under each copy set before writing

Exp. Number	Experiment Title/ Subject			3

Name		Lab Partner	Course	Section

COPY

Student's Signature		Date	Instructor/TA Signature		Date

Note: Insert Foldover Back flap under each copy set before writing

Exp. Number	Experiment Title/ Subject			4
Name		Lab Partner	Course	Section

Student's Signature	Date	Instructor/TA Signature	Date

Note: Insert Foldover Back flap under each copy set before writing

Exp. Number	Experiment Title/ Subject			4
Name		Lab Partner	Course	Section

Student's Signature	Date	Instructor/TA Signature	Date

Note: Insert Foldover Back flap under each copy set before writing

FOUNTAINHEAD PRESS

| Exp. Number | Experiment Title/ Subject | | | | 5 |
| Name | | Lab Partner | Course | Section | |

Exp. Number	Experiment Title/ Subject			5

Name		Lab Partner	Course	Section

COPY

Student's Signature		Date	Instructor/TA Signature		Date

Note: Insert Foldover Back flap under each copy set before writing

Exp. Number	Experiment Title/ Subject			6
Name		Lab Partner	Course	Section

Student's Signature	Date	Instructor/TA Signature	Date

Note: Insert Foldover Back flap under each copy set before writing

Exp. Number	Experiment Title/ Subject			
Name		Lab Partner	Course	Section

Student's Signature		Date	Instructor/TA Signature		Date

Note: Insert Foldover Back flap under each copy set before writing

Exp. Number	Experiment Title/ Subject			7
Name		Lab Partner	Course	Section

Student's Signature	Date	Instructor/TA Signature	Date

Note: Insert Foldover Back flap under each copy set before writing

Exp. Number	Experiment Title/ Subject			
Name		Lab Partner	Course	Section

COPY

Student's Signature		Date	Instructor/TA Signature	Date

Note: Insert Foldover Back flap under each copy set before writing

Exp. Number	Experiment Title/ Subject			8

Name		Lab Partner	Course	Section

Student's Signature	Date	Instructor/TA Signature	Date

Exp. Number	Experiment Title/ Subject			
Name		Lab Partner	Course	Section

Student's Signature		Date	Instructor/TA Signature		Date

Note: Insert Foldover Back flap under each copy set before writing

Exp. Number	Experiment Title/ Subject			9
Name		Lab Partner	Course	Section

Student's Signature		Date	Instructor/TA Signature		Date

Note: Insert Foldover Back flap under each copy set before writing

Exp. Number	Experiment Title/ Subject			9

Name		Lab Partner	Course	Section

COPY

Student's Signature		Date	Instructor/TA Signature		Date

Note: Insert Foldover Back flap under each copy set before writing

Exp. Number	Experiment Title/ Subject			10
Name		Lab Partner	Course	Section

Student's Signature	Date	Instructor/TA Signature	Date

Note: Insert Foldover Back flap under each copy set before writing

Exp. Number	Experiment Title/ Subject			
Name		Lab Partner	Course	Section

COPY

Student's Signature		Date	Instructor/TA Signature		Date

Note: Insert Foldover Back flap under each copy set before writing

Exp. Number	Experiment Title/ Subject			11
Name		Lab Partner	Course	Section

Student's Signature	Date	Instructor/TA Signature	Date

Note: Insert Foldover Back flap under each copy set before writing

Exp. Number	Experiment Title/ Subject			11

Name		Lab Partner	Course	Section

COPY

Student's Signature		Date	Instructor/TA Signature	Date

Note: Insert Foldover Back flap under each copy set before writing

Exp. Number	Experiment Title/ Subject			12
Name		Lab Partner	Course	Section

Note: Insert Foldover Back flap under each copy set before writing

FOUNTAINHEAD PRESS

Exp. Number	Experiment Title/ Subject			
Name		Lab Partner	Course	Section

Student's Signature	Date	Instructor/TA Signature	Date

Note: Insert Foldover Back flap under each copy set before writing

Exp. Number	Experiment Title/ Subject			13
Name		Lab Partner	Course	Section

Student's Signature	Date	Instructor/TA Signature	Date

Note: Insert Foldover Back flap under each copy set before writing

FOUNTAINHEAD PRESS

13

Exp. Number	Experiment Title/ Subject			
Name		Lab Partner	Course	Section

Student's Signature	Date	Instructor/TA Signature	Date

Note: Insert Foldover Back flap under each copy set before writing

FOUNTAINHEAD PRESS

Exp. Number	Experiment Title/ Subject			14

Name		Lab Partner	Course	Section

Student's Signature	Date	Instructor/TA Signature	Date

Note: Insert Foldover Back flap under each copy set before writing

Exp. Number	Experiment Title/ Subject			
Name		Lab Partner	Course	Section

Student's Signature		Date	Instructor/TA Signature		Date

Note: Insert Foldover Back flap under each copy set before writing

FOUNTAINHEAD PRESS

Exp. Number	Experiment Title/ Subject		15

Name		Lab Partner	Course	Section

Student's Signature	Date	Instructor/TA Signature	Date

Note: Insert Foldover Back flap under each copy set before writing

Exp. Number	Experiment Title/ Subject			15
Name		Lab Partner	Course	Section

Student's Signature	Date	Instructor/TA Signature	Date

Note: Insert Foldover Back flap under each copy set before writing

FOUNTAINHEAD PRESS

Exp. Number	Experiment Title/ Subject			16
Name		Lab Partner	Course	Section

Student's Signature	Date	Instructor/TA Signature	Date

Note: Insert Foldover Back flap under each copy set before writing

FOUNTAINHEAD PRESS

Exp. Number	Experiment Title/ Subject			16
Name		Lab Partner	Course	Section

Student's Signature	Date	Instructor/TA Signature	Date

Note: Insert Foldover Back flap under each copy set before writing

Exp. Number	Experiment Title/ Subject			17
Name		Lab Partner	Course	Section

Student's Signature	Date	Instructor/TA Signature	Date

Exp. Number	Experiment Title/ Subject			17
Name		Lab Partner	Course	Section

Student's Signature	Date	Instructor/TA Signature	Date

Note: Insert Foldover Back flap under each copy set before writing

FOUNTAINHEAD PRESS

Exp. Number	Experiment Title/ Subject		18

Name	Lab Partner	Course	Section

Student's Signature	Date	Instructor/TA Signature	Date

Note: Insert Foldover Back flap under each copy set before writing

Exp. Number	Experiment Title/ Subject			
Name		Lab Partner	Course	Section

COPY

Student's Signature		Date	Instructor/TA Signature		Date

Note: Insert Foldover Back flap under each copy set before writing

Exp. Number	Experiment Title/ Subject			19
Name		Lab Partner	Course	Section

Student's Signature	Date	Instructor/TA Signature	Date

Note: Insert Foldover Back flap under each copy set before writing

Exp. Number	Experiment Title/ Subject			19
Name		Lab Partner	Course	Section

Student's Signature	Date	Instructor/TA Signature	Date

COPY

Note: Insert Foldover Back flap under each copy set before writing

Exp. Number	Experiment Title/ Subject			20
Name		Lab Partner	Course	Section

Student's Signature	Date	Instructor/TA Signature	Date

Note: Insert Foldover Back flap under each copy set before writing

Exp. Number	Experiment Title/ Subject			20
Name		Lab Partner	Course	Section

Student's Signature	Date	Instructor/TA Signature	Date

Note: Insert Foldover Back flap under each copy set before writing

FOUNTAINHEAD PRESS

Exp. Number	Experiment Title/ Subject			21
Name		Lab Partner	Course	Section

Student's Signature	Date	Instructor/TA Signature	Date

FOUNTAINHEAD PRESS

Exp. Number	Experiment Title/ Subject			21

Name		Lab Partner	Course	Section

COPY

Student's Signature	Date	Instructor/TA Signature	Date

Note: Insert Foldover Back flap under each copy set before writing

Exp. Number	Experiment Title/ Subject			22
Name		Lab Partner	Course	Section

Student's Signature	Date	Instructor/TA Signature	Date

Note: Insert Foldover Back flap under each copy set before writing

22

Exp. Number	Experiment Title/ Subject			
Name		Lab Partner	Course	Section

COPY

Student's Signature	Date	Instructor/TA Signature	Date

Note: Insert Foldover Back flap under each copy set before writing

| Exp. Number | Experiment Title/ Subject | | | 23 |

| Name | | Lab Partner | Course | Section |

| Student's Signature | Date | Instructor/TA Signature | Date |

FOUNTAINHEAD PRESS

Exp. Number	Experiment Title/ Subject			23
Name		Lab Partner	Course	Section

Student's Signature	Date	Instructor/TA Signature	Date

COPY

Note: Insert Foldover Back flap under each copy set before writing

Exp. Number	Experiment Title/ Subject		24
Name		Lab Partner	Course	Section

Student's Signature	Date	Instructor/TA Signature	Date

Note: Insert Foldover Back flap under each copy set before writing

FOUNTAINHEAD PRESS

Exp. Number	Experiment Title/ Subject				24

Name		Lab Partner	Course	Section

COPY

Student's Signature		Date	Instructor/TA Signature		Date

Note: Insert Foldover Back flap under each copy set before writing

Exp. Number	Experiment Title/ Subject			25
Name		Lab Partner	Course	Section

Student's Signature	Date	Instructor/TA Signature	Date

Note: Insert Foldover Back flap under each copy set before writing

FOUNTAINHEAD PRESS

Exp. Number	Experiment Title/ Subject			25
Name		Lab Partner	Course	Section

Student's Signature	Date	Instructor/TA Signature	Date

Note: Insert Foldover Back flap under each copy set before writing

Exp. Number	Experiment Title/ Subject			26
Name		Lab Partner	Course	Section

Student's Signature	Date	Instructor/TA Signature	Date

Note: Insert Foldover Back flap under each copy set before writing

Exp. Number	Experiment Title/ Subject			
Name		Lab Partner	Course	Section

COPY

Student's Signature	Date	Instructor/TA Signature	Date

Note: Insert Foldover Back flap under each copy set before writing

Exp. Number	Experiment Title/ Subject			27
Name		Lab Partner	Course	Section

Student's Signature	Date	Instructor/TA Signature	Date

Note: Insert Foldover Back flap under each copy set before writing

Exp. Number	Experiment Title/ Subject			27
Name		Lab Partner	Course	Section

Student's Signature	Date	Instructor/TA Signature	Date

Note: Insert Foldover Back flap under each copy set before writing

Exp. Number	Experiment Title/ Subject			28

Name		Lab Partner	Course	Section

Student's Signature	Date	Instructor/TA Signature	Date

Note: Insert Foldover Back flap under each copy set before writing

Exp. Number	Experiment Title/ Subject			28

Name		Lab Partner	Course	Section

COPY

Student's Signature		Date	Instructor/TA Signature		Date

Note: Insert Foldover Back flap under each copy set before writing

Exp. Number	Experiment Title/ Subject			29
Name		Lab Partner	Course	Section

Student's Signature	Date	Instructor/TA Signature	Date

Note: Insert Foldover Back flap under each copy set before writing

Exp. Number	Experiment Title/ Subject			29
Name		Lab Partner	Course	Section

Student's Signature	Date	Instructor/TA Signature	Date

Note: Insert Foldover Back flap under each copy set before writing

Exp. Number	Experiment Title/ Subject			30
Name		Lab Partner	Course	Section

Student's Signature	Date	Instructor/TA Signature	Date

Note: Insert Foldover Back flap under each copy set before writing

Exp. Number	Experiment Title/ Subject			30

Name		Lab Partner	Course	Section

COPY

Student's Signature		Date	Instructor/TA Signature	Date

Note: Insert Foldover Back flap under each copy set before writing

Exp. Number	Experiment Title/ Subject			31
Name		Lab Partner	Course	Section

Student's Signature	Date	Instructor/TA Signature	Date

Note: Insert Foldover Back flap under each copy set before writing

Exp. Number	Experiment Title/ Subject			
Name		Lab Partner	Course	Section

Student's Signature		Date	Instructor/TA Signature		Date

Note: Insert Foldover Back flap under each copy set before writing

Exp. Number	Experiment Title/ Subject			32
Name		Lab Partner	Course	Section

Student's Signature	Date	Instructor/TA Signature	Date

Note: Insert Foldover Back flap under each copy set before writing

Exp. Number	Experiment Title/ Subject			32
Name		Lab Partner	Course	Section

COPY

Student's Signature	Date	Instructor/TA Signature	Date

Note: Insert Foldover Back flap under each copy set before writing

Exp. Number	Experiment Title/ Subject			33
Name		Lab Partner	Course	Section

Student's Signature	Date	Instructor/TA Signature	Date

Note: Insert Foldover Back flap under each copy set before writing

FOUNTAINHEAD PRESS

Exp. Number	Experiment Title/ Subject			33

Name	Lab Partner	Course	Section

COPY

Student's Signature	Date	Instructor/TA Signature	Date

Note: Insert Foldover Back flap under each copy set before writing

Exp. Number	Experiment Title/ Subject				34
Name		Lab Partner	Course	Section	

Student's Signature	Date	Instructor/TA Signature	Date

Note: Insert Foldover Back flap under each copy set before writing

Exp. Number	Experiment Title/ Subject			
				34
Name		Lab Partner	Course	Section

COPY

Student's Signature	Date	Instructor/TA Signature	Date

Note: Insert Foldover Back flap under each copy set before writing

Exp. Number	Experiment Title/ Subject				35
Name		Lab Partner	Course	Section	

Student's Signature	Date	Instructor/TA Signature	Date

Note: Insert Foldover Back flap under each copy set before writing

Exp. Number	Experiment Title/ Subject			35

Name		Lab Partner	Course	Section

COPY

Student's Signature	Date	Instructor/TA Signature	Date

Note: Insert Foldover Back flap under each copy set before writing

Exp. Number	Experiment Title/ Subject			36
Name		Lab Partner	Course	Section

Student's Signature	Date	Instructor/TA Signature	Date

Note: Insert Foldover Back flap under each copy set before writing

Exp. Number	Experiment Title/ Subject			
Name		Lab Partner	Course	Section

Student's Signature	Date	Instructor/TA Signature	Date

Note: Insert Foldover Back flap under each copy set before writing

Exp. Number	Experiment Title/ Subject			37
Name		Lab Partner	Course	Section

Student's Signature	Date	Instructor/TA Signature	Date

Note: Insert Foldover Back flap under each copy set before writing

Exp. Number	Experiment Title/ Subject			37
Name		Lab Partner	Course	Section

Student's Signature	Date	Instructor/TA Signature	Date

Note: Insert Foldover Back flap under each copy set before writing

Exp. Number	Experiment Title/ Subject			38
Name		Lab Partner	Course	Section

Student's Signature	Date	Instructor/TA Signature	Date

Note: Insert Foldover Back flap under each copy set before writing

Exp. Number	Experiment Title/ Subject			
Name		Lab Partner	Course	Section

COPY

Student's Signature	Date	Instructor/TA Signature	Date

Note: Insert Foldover Back flap under each copy set before writing

Exp. Number	Experiment Title/ Subject			39
Name		Lab Partner	Course	Section

Exp. Number	Experiment Title/ Subject			39
Name		Lab Partner	Course	Section

Student's Signature	Date	Instructor/TA Signature	Date

Note: Insert Foldover Back flap under each copy set before writing

Exp. Number	Experiment Title/ Subject			40
Name		Lab Partner	Course	Section

Student's Signature	Date	Instructor/TA Signature	Date

Note: Insert Foldover Back flap under each copy set before writing

FOUNTAINHEAD PRESS

40

Exp. Number	Experiment Title/ Subject			
Name		Lab Partner	Course	Section

40

Note: Insert Foldover Back flap under each copy set before writing

Exp. Number	Experiment Title/ Subject		41

Name	Lab Partner	Course	Section

Student's Signature	Date	Instructor/TA Signature	Date

Note: Insert Foldover Back flap under each copy set before writing

Exp. Number	Experiment Title/ Subject			41
Name		Lab Partner	Course	Section

Student's Signature	Date	Instructor/TA Signature	Date

Note: Insert Foldover Back flap under each copy set before writing

FOUNTAINHEAD PRESS

Exp. Number	Experiment Title/ Subject			42
Name		Lab Partner	Course	Section

Student's Signature	Date	Instructor/TA Signature	Date

Note: Insert Foldover Back flap under each copy set before writing

FOUNTAINHEAD PRESS

Exp. Number	Experiment Title/ Subject				42
Name		Lab Partner	Course	Section	

COPY

Student's Signature		Date	Instructor/TA Signature		Date

Note: Insert Foldover Back flap under each copy set before writing

FOUNTAINHEAD PRESS

Exp. Number	Experiment Title/ Subject			43
Name		Lab Partner	Course	Section

Student's Signature	Date	Instructor/TA Signature	Date

Note: Insert Foldover Back flap under each copy set before writing

Exp. Number	Experiment Title/ Subject			43
Name		Lab Partner	Course	Section

Student's Signature	Date	Instructor/TA Signature	Date

Note: Insert Foldover Back flap under each copy set before writing

Exp. Number	Experiment Title/ Subject			44
Name		Lab Partner	Course	Section

Student's Signature	Date	Instructor/TA Signature	Date

Note: Insert Foldover Back flap under each copy set before writing

Exp. Number	Experiment Title/ Subject			
Name		Lab Partner	Course	Section

44

Student's Signature	Date	Instructor/TA Signature	Date

Note: Insert Foldover Back flap under each copy set before writing

FOUNTAINHEAD PRESS

Exp. Number	Experiment Title/ Subject			4 5
Name		Lab Partner	Course	Section

Student's Signature	Date	Instructor/TA Signature	Date

Note: Insert Foldover Back flap under each copy set before writing

FOUNTAINHEAD PRESS

Exp. Number	Experiment Title/ Subject			45
Name		Lab Partner	Course	Section

COPY

Student's Signature	Date	Instructor/TA Signature	Date

Note: Insert Foldover Back flap under each copy set before writing

Exp. Number	Experiment Title/ Subject			46
Name		Lab Partner	Course	Section

Student's Signature		Date	Instructor/TA Signature		Date

Note: Insert Foldover Back flap under each copy set before writing

Exp. Number	Experiment Title/ Subject			
Name		Lab Partner	Course	Section

Student's Signature		Date	Instructor/TA Signature		Date

Note: Insert Foldover Back flap under each copy set before writing

Exp. Number	Experiment Title/ Subject			47
Name		Lab Partner	Course	Section

Note: Insert Foldover Back flap under each copy set before writing

FOUNTAINHEAD PRESS

Exp. Number	Experiment Title/ Subject			47

Name		Lab Partner	Course	Section

COPY

Student's Signature	Date	Instructor/TA Signature	Date

Note: Insert Foldover Back flap under each copy set before writing

Exp. Number	Experiment Title/ Subject			48
Name		Lab Partner	Course	Section

Student's Signature	Date	Instructor/TA Signature	Date

Note: Insert Foldover Back flap under each copy set before writing

FOUNTAINHEAD PRESS

Exp. Number	Experiment Title/ Subject			
Name		Lab Partner	Course	Section

Student's Signature	Date	Instructor/TA Signature	Date

Note: Insert Foldover Back flap under each copy set before writing

Exp. Number	Experiment Title/ Subject				49
Name		Lab Partner	Course	Section	

Student's Signature	Date	Instructor/TA Signature	Date

Note: Insert Foldover Back flap under each copy set before writing

Exp. Number	Experiment Title/ Subject			
Name		**Lab Partner**	**Course**	**Section**

COPY

Student's Signature	Date	Instructor/TA Signature	Date

Note: Insert Foldover Back flap under each copy set before writing

Exp. Number	Experiment Title/ Subject			50
Name		Lab Partner	Course	Section

Student's Signature	Date	Instructor/TA Signature	Date

Note: Insert Foldover Back flap under each copy set before writing

FOUNTAINHEAD PRESS

Exp. Number	Experiment Title/ Subject			50
Name		Lab Partner	Course	Section

COPY

Student's Signature	Date	Instructor/TA Signature	Date

Note: Insert Foldover Back flap under each copy set before writing